THE BATTLE FOR THE BROADS

Overleaf: *Cruising on
the Norfolk Broads*
Eastern Daily Press

THE BATTLE FOR THE BROADS

A History of Environmental Degradation
and Renewal

Martin Ewans

TERENCE DALTON LIMITED
LAVENHAM, SUFFOLK 1992

Published by
TERENCE DALTON LIMITED
ISBN 0 86138 092 4 hardback
　　　0 86138 095 9 limp covers

Text photoset in 10/11 pt Baskerville
Printed in Great Britain at
The Lavenham Press Limited, Lavenham, Suffolk

Contents

Preface

MARTIN Ewans has written a scholarly but highly readable account of the evolution of the Broads from the earliest times to the present day. His work therefore encompasses the high points in the history of this unique system of waterways as well as the grievous threats to which it has more recently been exposed.

The Norfolk Society, as the local branch of the Council for the Protection of Rural England, is proud to have played a part in recognizing and meeting these threats. The Society most gladly commends the outstanding contribution Martin Ewans has made to the better understanding of a much cherished part of our heritage. It should inspire Norfolk people, and many others, to maintain their vigilance in the years to come and to ensure the preservation of a wonderful asset.

General Sir Harry Tuzo
President, The Norfolk Society (CPRE)

★

Acknowledgements

I AM INDEBTED to a large number of people for their assistance and advice over the preparation of this book. In particular, I am grateful to Richard Hobbs of the Norfolk Naturalists' Trust and Hugh Murland of the Norfolk Society for reading the manuscript and suggesting corrections and improvements. The responsibility for errors of fact and judgement, however, is mine alone.

No writer of a book such as this can fail to be indebted also to the many authors who have contributed to what has over the years become an extensive Broads literature. Much of this literature is mentioned in the text or in the bibliography at the end, while several of the authors, notably the Broadland naturalists, are dealt with at length. There are, however, a few "Broads people" of whom particular mention must be made. The first is Dr Joyce Lambert, who was responsible, with a group of fellow researchers, for the demonstration that the broads had their origins as abandoned peat diggings (chapter one). The outcome of their researches, in which they revised their earlier endorsement of the common assumption that the broads were merely lakes left behind by the sea as it receded from the Broadland estuary, was published in the Royal Geographical Society's Research Memoir no 3 of 1960, *The Making of the Broads: a Reconsideration in the Light of New Evidence*. A summary of this memoir is given in E. A. Ellis's book, *The Broads*, published in 1965.

Mention must also be made of the group of researchers, many from the University of East Anglia, who between them established the causes of the ecological deterioration of the Broads (chapter seven). They include R. F. Bryant, R. C. Hoather, P. A. Holdway, C. F. Mason, B. Moss and R. A. Watson. Several of their research papers were published in *Freshwater Biology* and *Biological Conservation*.

The experts on the British National Parks (chapter ten) are Ann and Malcolm MacEwen. Their critiques of the system are contained in *National Parks: Conservation or Cosmetics?* (Allen and Unwin, 1982) and *Greenprints for the Countryside* (Allen and Unwin, 1987).

Professor O'Riordan, who is Chairman of the Environment Committee of the Broads Authority, has chronicled the Halvergate affair (chapters thirteen and fourteen) in a number of articles; see *ECOS* 2(2), 1981, *The Countryman*, Spring 1983 and *ECOS* 6(1), 1985. An account of the earlier, confrontational stages of the controversy is also given in *Countryside Conflicts* by Philip Lowe and others, published in 1986 by the Gower Publishing Co. Ltd.

The Royal Society for Nature Conservation's seminal policy statement, *Nature Conservation and Agriculture* (chapter eighteen) was published in June 1988.

The author is grateful to the following for photographs and diagrams: Anglia Television, Broads Authority, Council for the Protection of Rural England, Department of Geography, University of Nottingham, *Eastern Daily Press*, Paul Ewans, Ida Grosvenor, F. G. Kitton, Bob Malster, J. R. Marr, Cliff Middleton, *New Scientist*, Norfolk Library Services, Norfolk Museums Service, Norfolk Naturalists' Trust, Vincent and Linda Pargeter, Public Records Office, Royal Society for the Protection of Birds, Michael Seago, *Times Newspapers Ltd*, Martin Trelawney, Philip Wayre of the Otter Trust and Ivan West.

The diagram on page 85 is from *Wetland Ecology* by J. R. Etherington and is reproduced by kind permission of Edward Arnold (Publishers) Ltd.

★

Introduction

THE VIEW from the tower of the Church of St Helen, Ranworth, is one of the loveliest in England. Close below sparkle two of the most attractive broads, Malthouse Broad and Ranworth Broad itself. Beyond them, over an arc of several miles stretching from the east round to the north-west, lie Ranworth and Woodbastwick Marshes, a wide chequerboard of greens, golds and browns, of woodland, reed beds and alder carr. Through these marshes flows the River Bure, gleaming in short stretches as it winds through the trees. Some two miles to the north-east are the ruins of St Benet's Abbey, lying on the north bank of the Bure where the fen gives way to an equally wide expanse of grazing marsh. From the Abbey, where a large wooden cross marks the site of the high altar, the fresh green of the meadows runs towards the east and the north-east, beyond the Bure and its tributaries, the Ant and the Thurne, until the flatness gives way to the low hills of Ludham and Flegg. Over to the north-west, beyond Woodbastwick Fen, is the riverside village of Horning; and beyond it is Wroxham, the main "gateway" to the Broads. To the south of Ranworth the countryside is a patchwork of fields and orchards, hedges and copses, stretching in low folds up to the watershed that divides the valley of the Bure from that of the Yare. As everywhere in Norfolk, villages near and far can be located by the towers of their churches, perhaps some dozen or so in all, while a number of wind-driven drainage pumps, several of them now in ruins, mark the boundaries between the rivers and the grazing marshes.

It is all a scene of great peace and beauty, overarched by the wide and luminous Norfolk sky. But these northern broads, while possibly the best known, are by no means the whole. To the south, the Yare and the Waveney meander through their own wide valleys, until they join at Breydon Water and finally arrive at Yarmouth, where fierce tides make for a notoriously difficult passage to and from the Bure. To the north-east lies the great complex of Hickling Broad, Horsey Mere and Heigham Sound, with fens and marshes precariously separated from the North Sea by a low fringe of dunes. Out of view to the south-east are Halvergate Marshes, which form one of the largest expanses of grazing marsh in the British Isles. And there is much more: Barton Broad and the northern reaches of the Ant; the "Trinity" Broads, Filby, Rollesby and Ormesby; Fritton Decoy and Oulton Broad behind Lowestoft; and many hidden places such as the Hardley Flood, Upton Fen and Cockshoot Broad.

For centuries Broadland was largely isolated and unremarked. Yarmouth thrived on its fishing and Norwich was at one time second only to London in wealth and population. But their prosperity barely extended to the countryside between, where a small population eked out a meagre existence from farm and smallholding, wildfowl, osier, reed and fish. Then, in the nineteenth century, the Broads began to attract the sportsman, the naturalist and the yachtsman. Many notable British naturalists, including the Reverend Richard Lubbock, Arthur Patterson and later Ted Ellis, studied and described the immense and often unique variety of the flora and fauna of the area. Conservation measures were progressively introduced and reserves created, but there was nothing adequate to protect the Broads from the postwar consequences of the growth of population, the revolution in farming methods and the wholesale expansion of the yachting and motor-boat industry. Over the past forty years, this area of great natural beauty and wealth of flora and fauna has been gravely damaged and only gradually and with great difficulty have steps been taken and institutions created to introduce some overall measure of control. It was not until 1988 that a status was given to the Broads comparable with that of a National Park.

It has been a story of conflict and compromise, of typically British muddle, apathy and half-measures, of uncoordinated campaigners and organised vested interests. But it has also been a story of vision, will and persistence, of collective and individual effort and of some degree of progress. Above all, it is a story not yet fully told.

The aims of this book, therefore, are fourfold. The first is to describe the Broads as they once were: how they came into existence, how they related to the surrounding areas and places further afield, the way of life of those who lived in them, whether as marshmen or watermen, and the manner in which they have changed during the last two centuries. The second aim is to examine the deterioration of their natural environment—what has been called, in the words of one expert, "a classic example of ecological degradation"—and to assess its causes. The third is to review the long process, essentially political in nature, which has led to their being given some measure of protection, with the establishment of a statutory Broads Authority. The final aim is to draw conclusions, within this historical, environmental and political context, about the problems encountered, and those still to be faced, in trying to achieve an acceptable measure of conservation in what are not only arguably the most important wetlands of the British Isles, but also the only National Park (in all but name) that has been created in Britain for more than thirty years.

PART ONE

THE VIRGINAL BROADS

The Origins of the Broads   1

There must have been a period of about five hundred years—shall we say, very roughly, between the time of Alfred the Great and Henry the Fifth—during which it was possible to dig peat in East Norfolk to a depth of ten feet or more.

Eastern Daily Press

An intriguing geological and historical process has led to the creation of Broadland. At the time of the Roman occupation of Britain, during roughly the first six centuries of the modern era, there was a single "Great Estuary" where the Broads now lie; it was known to the Romans as Gariensis. This estuary was large and complex, with its principal mouth stretching from what is now Caister-on-Sea southwards across the whole of present-day Great Yarmouth. There were probably several outflows to the north, between Martham and Waxham, and possibly a further one to the south, at Oulton and Lowestoft. Inland, the estuary may have reached some miles up the valleys of the Yare, the Bure, the Ant and the Waveney. It was probably at its widest extent during the Iron Age, and by Roman times was once again gradually becoming silted up as the relative sea level slowly fell. A triangle of mudflats may have extended towards the sea from a base lying between Reedham and Acle, and a "middle ground" was spreading beyond the apex of these flats in the lower estuary.

The uplands around the estuary were thinly populated, as they had been for many centuries previously, with extensive areas of heath and woodland. The site of the regional capital, Venta Icenorum, can still be seen at Caistor St Edmund, a few miles south of present-day Norwich, and there may have been smaller Roman settlements on the fringes of the estuary, at Reedham, Brundall and Thorpe. The other main town was at Caister-on-Sea on the northern shore of the estuary. Excavations there have shown the existence of a Romano-Saxon walled town extending to some thirty-five acres, with a paved road running down to an anchorage immediately to the south. Caister was founded in the second century AD but was still a flourishing settlement in the fourth century; it seems to have continued as such, as a Saxon town, for a

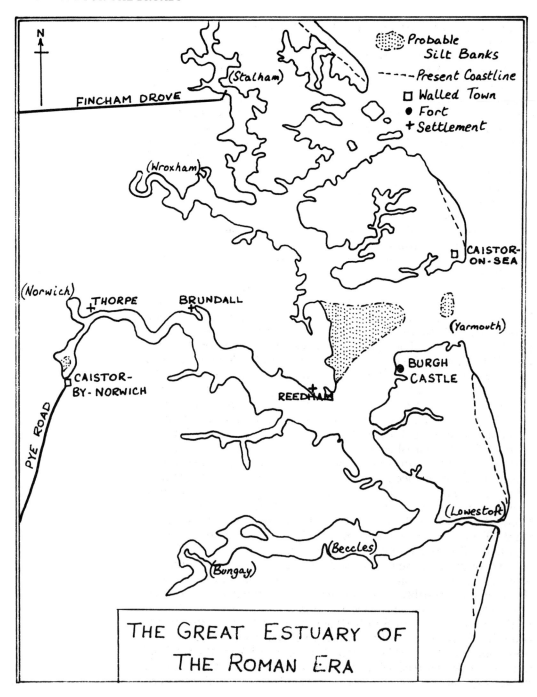

THE GREAT ESTUARY OF
THE ROMAN ERA

further appreciable period. With a well-sheltered anchorage close to the sea—an advantage which other east-coast Roman ports did not share—it is easy to see why it was a thriving centre. North of Caister-on-Sea, the Flegg "island" seems to have been virtually uninhabited and of economic importance only by reason of the port, which provided a secure haven at a convenient point for the sea crossing to Flanders and the Rhineland. Later in the Roman era East Anglia was threatened by Anglo-Saxon invaders, and to guard against them Burgh Castle was built late in the third century on the southern shore of the estuary, as one of a chain of substantial fortresses stretching from Portchester in Portsmouth Harbour to Brancaster on the north Norfolk coast. The impressive walls of this fortress, which was known to the Romans as Gariannonum, enclose an area of some six acres on a bluff overlooking the lower reaches of the Waveney and Breydon Water. It was under the command of an officer with the romantic-sounding title of "The Count of the Saxon Shore" and was the base for a squadron of Stablesian Horse, as well as for a contingent of the "British Fleet".

As the Roman period neared its end in the fifth century AD, so the Anglo-Saxon forays against East Anglia developed into a period of more permanent occupation. Many Anglo-Saxons sailed into the Great Estuary and settled near its shores. For two or three hundred years they had the region largely to themselves, but they were joined late in the eighth century by Danish colonists, many of whose villages are to be found in Broadland, particularly in the Flegg peninsula. In contrast to the Roman period, by the time of the Norman Conquest not only was Norfolk one of the most densely populated parts of England but within Norfolk the most populous areas were those of the Flegg Hundred and the Happing Hundred, in the parishes lying between Waxham and Yarmouth. There was also an unusually high proportion of freemen there, which may have been another consequence of the Danish settlement. The area was rich in meadows and carried large numbers of sheep. Salt-making was a thriving industry, and Domesday Book records a series of evaporating salt pans on the Bure, from Runham near its mouth to as far upstream as South Walsham. Caister alone had forty-five such pans.

Throughout these centuries the relative levels of land and sea were progressively changing, and by the time of Domesday Book the land was probably at the highest relative point it has reached since Iron Age times. Excavations at Yarmouth for the foundations of the power station at South Denes exposed beach deposits that could be accurately dated from the potsherds found in them, and they show conclusively that in the thirteenth century the sea level was some thirteen feet below that of the present day. One cause of its subsequent rise is that for a long while England has been

Regatta at Wroxham: Wroxham Broad, Hoveton Great Broad and Salhouse Broad. This picture (taken in 1936) shows clearly that the river runs alongside, rather than through, the broads.
Norfolk Library Services

progressively tilting from west to east. The relative sea level has in fact shown appreciable changes in both directions over the past few millennia, so that the possibility of a rise in ocean levels in the not too distant future is nothing new.

It is these changes in sea level that account for the creation of the broads—but not, as was thought until about thirty years ago, simply through their having been left as residual lakes after the fall in water level and shrinkage of the estuary. Rather, it has been established by means of some comprehensive and elegant research that they are the flooded remains of medieval peat diggings. The evidence for this comes from many sources, archaeological, geological and documentary. First, it is well attested that there was significant use of peat in the area in medieval times. For example, the accounts of Norwich Cathedral Priory for the late thirteenth and fourteenth centuries show that peat was used for the kitchens there on an extensive scale—up to 400,000 turves in a single year. There is also evidence of a trade in peat in the area during this period: at both Norwich and Yarmouth, for example, murage (a tax levied on goods brought into and out of towns, in order to pay for the upkeep of the walls) was charged on the carriage of peat. The deeds of several Broadland manors, again in roughly the same period, show that they possessed turbaries (as the peat diggings were then called); one such was the Manor of Burgh Vaux in Flegg Hundred, which owned land in the area of the Trinity Broads. Manorial sales are also well attested: the sale of over 200,000 turves a year are, for example, recorded from South Walsham in the latter half of the thirteenth century. Grants of turbary and disputes over it feature in the "cartulary", or records, of St Benet's Abbey in the twelfth century. Turbary is mentioned in documents relating to no fewer than twenty places around Broadland, all of them containing broads or parts of broads; in several, the proportion of turbary to arable land was between twenty and forty per cent. Taking all the documentary evidence available there is no doubt that peat was produced in very substantial quantities around Broadland, in places where broads now exist, from roughly the middle of the twelfth century until well into the fifteenth.

Some aspects of this production are particularly interesting. In the first place, not only is it contemporaneous with the final centuries of the marine regression, at the point where the land would have been at its highest level relative to the sea, but references to peat diggings begin to die out as the relative sea level once again rose. Thus the accounts of the cellarers of Norwich Cathedral Priory show that peat was gradually replaced by wood and other fuels in the late fourteenth and fifteenth centuries. There is also some evidence that towards the end of the period methods of extracting peat began to change, and that it was increasingly a question of dredging peat from waterlogged areas, rather than of cutting turves from fairly solid beds. For example, in Barton Broad in the late fourteenth and fifteenth centuries, turf was being dredged from water in which fisheries were clearly a more important source of income. A particularly significant date is 1287, when the sea broke into the Broads area and caused widespread flooding, a vivid account of which is given by one of the monks of St Benet's Abbey, John of Oxenedes; this was possibly a critical date in the decline of the Broadland peat industry. There is little evidence of turf-cutting after 1500 and it does not feature at all in the relatively abundant survey books of the sixteenth century.

On the other side of the coin, and further suggesting that the broads derived from these peat diggings, there is no documentary or other evidence of the existence of any of the broads before the fourteenth century. There is a reference to a "Brodingge" at South Walsham early in that century, but it is not until the fifteenth and sixteenth centuries that reliable evidence begins to appear in the form of representations of some of the broads on maps and references in documents to "fisheries", "water" and "waterground" in contexts where they can confidently be taken to refer to broads rather than to rivers. In a few cases, the transition of a piece of land from turbary to "water and fen" can be traced in legal documents. There is thus a fairly clear historical sequence in the relevant places of peat diggings first and broads only subsequently. At Burgh Vaux, for example, there is by the fifteenth century no longer any mention of turf production, but fisheries do now feature. It was not until the time of Elizabeth I that there are any documentary references to broads that are named as such.

The decisive evidence, however, comes from detailed surveys of many of the broads which were begun by Dr Joyce Lambert in the 1950s. Dr Lambert, a botanist by profession, was at the time studying plant successions in peat deposits and for this purpose making a series of closely spaced borings around Surlingham Broad on the Yare. So surprising were her profiles of broads and peat beds that she repeated the borings elsewhere, with very similar results. Eventually, some two thousand hand borings were made across the Broadland valleys and broads, which revealed a succession of profiles quite incompatible with the theory that the broads were natural lakes. For example, below an infilling of mud their peat bottoms were remarkably level at a depth of between eight and twelve feet, and their sides tended to be vertical or stepped except where they extended to the gravel valley slopes. They were all either in side valleys or to the side of the main stream of the nearest river and divided from it by banks or "ronds". Many of them were situated at points where the most recent layer of estuarine clay, laid down in Roman times, was either thin or non-existent, so that it was no difficult matter to dig through the top post-Roman layer of peat into the thick layer of alderwood, sedge and reed peat below. Even more significantly, several of them possessed peat islands with nearly vertical sides and were crossed by several roughly parallel peat balks, the lines of some of which coincided with the boundaries of land holdings shown on medieval estate maps.

The conclusion from this evidence, as well as from all the historical and documentary sources, has to be that the Broads are peat diggings which were flooded and then abandoned as the water levels rose. One estimate is that some nine million cubic feet of peat must have been extracted from perhaps more than 2,500 acres over several centuries of major peat extraction from Broadland in medieval times.

★　★　★

The first documentary reference to a broad: an extract from a valuation, dated 1315, of parts of a manor at South Walsham. This refers to pasture at "Brodiggen" (end of line eleven), as well as to turbaries at several places close to the present broad. Two of them, "Harefen" and "Woodfen", still carry the same names.
Public Records Office

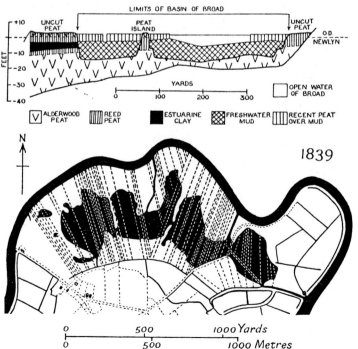

The broads as peat diggings. This simplified cross-section of Hoveton Great Broad reveals characteristics suggesting that it must have originated as a peat digging. The sides are near vertical; the bottom is relatively flat below an infilling of mud, which cuts through the layers of peat; and there is a steep-sided "island" of uncut peat in the centre.
New Scientist

Several broads contain peninsulas and islands which align with property boundaries. This tithe map of Surlingham Broad shows clear signs of strip-parcelling of turbary rights.
New Scientist

7

The Traditional Life of Broadland: the Marshland Economy   2

The men who lived in isolated cottages on the lonesome marshes, and spent days and nights on the rivers and fens, were of a freedom-loving and self-reliant type. Leaving to others the waging of war, the tilling of land, the reaping of corn, they endured shivering fits of ague, scorching blaze of summer sun and numbing blast of winter wind, because the fascination of an unfettered life had cast its spell upon them. Busy with their nets, traps and decoys, they were content to have no part in the doings of the world which lay beyond the horizon of their familiar marshes. For their life was far from being monotonous: every season, and almost every month of the year, brought them change of occupation . . . Their methods of gaining a livelihood made them close observers of the habits of fish, bird and beast; the knowledge of natural history that was lost when an aged Broadsman died . . . would, if printed, have made his name famous. They were flight shooters, punt-gunners, eel-catchers, fish-netters, reed-cutters, dyke-drawers and cattle-tenders. Frequently one man, in the course of twelve months, would be engaged in each and all of these pursuits and occupations.

W. A. Dutt

On the uplands and river slopes of the Broadland region, the patterns of farming and village life would have been very much the same after the creation of the Broads as they had been for many centuries previously. As elsewhere in Norfolk, some villages moved or disappeared over the years, in some cases possibly as a consequence of the Black Death in the fourteenth century, but many of the Broadland villages that persist to the present day were founded in Saxon times and are recorded in Domesday Book. The main focus of the region was of course Norwich, with its castle and cathedral, the seat of both civil and ecclesiastical power. But as the medieval era progressed, Yarmouth and Lowestoft became increasingly busy ports, and Beccles and Bungay significant towns. Several market centres also grew up at convenient distances apart. For example, there used to be a market at Hickling, which was

Opposite:
Gunner working up to fowl. P. H. Emerson's photograph, although obviously posed, portrays the gunner's technique to perfection.

granted an annual three-day fair in the reign of Henry III; the market at Acle is still in existence, although a shadow of its former self.

Up to the time of the Dissolution, much influence was wielded in Broadland by the monastic houses, of which the best known is that of St Benet-at-Holm, a holm being a small area of dry land set among the fens. At the time of the flooding of the Broads in 1912, the then vicar of Potter Heigham reported seeing the whole of the valley from Thurne across to Ludham and Horning covered with water, with only the site of St Benet's emerging from the flood, its encircling ring of thorn trees marking the line of the old precinct wall. A small number of Saxon monks founded a settlement there in the ninth century, but this was destroyed by Viking invaders in 870. Early in the eleventh century it was refounded by King Canute as a Benedictine abbey, and it became wealthy and prestigious over the years. He endowed it with the manors of Horning, Ludham and Neatishead, and it subsequently received many gifts of churches, rents and lands, eventually becoming the richest monastic establishment in Norfolk after Walsingham. Rents were paid in money, services or kind: land at Potter Heigham, for instance, provided the monks with an annual supply of ale. The abbey was not above encroaching on common rights in its vicinity, including, according to a special commission appointed by King Edward I, those of fishing in Wroxham Broad and in the river between Wroxham and Acle bridges. Of those buried at St Benet's, one of the better known is Sir John Fastolff, a valiant warrior who fought at Agincourt and bore no resemblance at all to Shakespeare's caricature. Much of his castle at Caister still remains and can be visited.

Other monastic houses existed at Acle, Herringfleet, Aldeby, Hickling, Bungay, Ingham and Langley, as well as in Norwich and Yarmouth; these had a significant economic, in addition to a spiritual, influence on the region. Langley Priory was another favourite interment place for the nobility of Norfolk and owned no fewer than nineteen manors across the county. What remains of it is now incorporated into farm buildings. Of these monastic houses, St Benet's was unique in escaping dissolution in 1539; the Abbot had just been consecrated Bishop of Norwich and was able to do a deal with the King (to the latter's advantage) whereby he kept the property of the abbey but relinquished to the King the possessions of the bishopric. The Bishop of Norwich is consequently to this day also the Abbot of St Benet's. But the abbey ceased functioning before many years had passed and its stonework was exhaustively plundered. As late as the nineteen-twenties many of the buildings in Horning and elsewhere in the neighbourhood sported gargoyles and other evidence of their construction from stone from St Benet's.

Each Broadland village also had its church, often of Saxon origin; because some areas of Broadland did not subsequently enjoy the prosperity brought by the wool trade to other parts of East Anglia many churches have retained an unusually large share of their Saxon and Norman features. Their relative smallness may also be due to the fact that there were few great estates in Broadland, unlike some other areas of Norfolk. Where, however, the wool trade thrived or there was an association with a monastery or bishopric, churches were rebuilt on a lavish scale, in Decorated or Perpendicular style. From some of them it is possible to gain a fascinating insight into the beliefs of their medieval congregations, particularly where, as at Ranworth and Barton Turf, decorated rood screens have survived, or where, as at West Somerton and Wickhampton, wall paintings have been uncovered.

Over the centuries, the lives of the great mass of Broadland inhabitants were undoubtedly hard. The bigger landowners, both lay and ecclesiastical, did well except in times of extreme economic adversity, as did those artisans and entrepreneurs connected with the wool trade. But life was never easy for the peasant farmer or the landless labourer. Local power was in the hands of the lords of the manor, who thrived at first on forced labour and later on rental income. As a result of the wool trade and of agricultural

The rood screen at Ranworth Church.
P. A. Ewans

improvement they did particularly well in the sixteenth and seventeenth centuries, and many of them fulfilled what they saw as their duties to their less fortunate neighbours in a benevolent and paternalistic way. But there can be little doubt that men from the Broads participated in the Litester Rebellion of 1381 and Kett's Rebellion of 1549, both of which were only put down after Norwich had been occupied. During the Litester rising, St Benet's Abbey was besieged and was forced to surrender all the documents of land title it possessed; while among the demands of the rebels during the Kett revolt were, significantly, that the "redegrounde and meadow-grounde may be at such price as they were in the first yere of Kyng Henry the VII" and that "ryvers may be ffre and comon to all men for fyshyng and passage". Between the sixteenth and nineteenth centuries malaria, or "ague", was prevalent around the Broads and added to the miseries of the inhabitants, who must also have suffered more generally from the dampness of the region. Opium seems often to have been used as a palliative. Curiously there are no records of any earlier existence of malaria, and the reasons for its disappearance are equally obscure.

When the Enclosure Acts were passed in the late eighteenth and early nineteenth centuries there took place what Walter Rye has called "undignified scrambles for open land" in which "everyone of any importance was bribed to silence by a good slice for himself", with the result that the people at large were deprived of some fifty per cent of their common rights and had thereafter to rely on inadequate "poor allotments". As from elsewhere in Norfolk and Suffolk, there was a substantial emigration to the New World in the nineteenth century, the incomes of the farm workers often being insufficient for basic family needs. Many of the emigrants sailed from Yarmouth.

Sharing these vicissitudes over the centuries, there lived and worked on the margins and within the river valleys of Broadland a unique breed of men, the marshmen. They were a versatile race, dependent on a variety of occupations according to the time of year. Their lives were remote and solitary, and many of them came from a small number of extended families, the occupation being handed down from father to son. Their farmsteads and cottages, which tended to be described by outsiders as "picturesque", were a favourite subject for members of the Norwich School of painters, who were greatly attracted by the bucolic riverside scenes which were to be found within easy reach of the city. R. H. Mottram gives this description of a marshman's cottage:

> Across the few yards of "rond" or firm riverside embankment was a wooden paling enclosing a small garden, above which was a typical Broadland labourer's cottage, whitewashed, covered as if with some immense greeny-brown drapery with heavy sagging thatch, its "clay-

lump" walls held in place by the massive brick chimney that formed one end, and the wash-house, containing the brick copper, at the other. The building between these supports had thus one "all-purposes" living room, with a window beside the door and another opposite, and another door giving upon a corkscrew stair contrived around a stalwart timber, that led to two bedrooms below the rafters, the little old square lattice windows of these being on a level with their floor.

Such a cottage, known as "Toad Hall Cottage", has been preserved and is still to be seen at How Hill on the River Ant. Elsewhere, the marshmen's cottages were noted as being "thatched part with straw, part with sedge, and having curious names, like the 'Devil's House' or the 'Monkey's House', some almost ruinous, some propped up". In addition to the picturesqueness, it would be realistic to concede an element of squalor.

The marshmen's principal occupation was the tending of cattle and sheep on the grazing marshes. In medieval times the marshes were probably used as rough grazing for local cattle, but in later years many of the cattle tended by the marshmen came from Scotland and Wales. They were driven down through England on a network of "droves", to be auctioned in the spring and early summer at Horsham St Faith's just north of Norwich. A vivid account of the trade was given by Daniel Defoe in 1724:

The river Yare runs through this city and is navigable thus far without the help of any art (that is to say, without locks or stops) and being increased by other waters, passes afterwards through a long tract of the richest meadows and the largest, take them altogether, that are anywhere in England, lying for thirty miles in length from this city to Yarmouth, including the return of the said meadows on the bank of the Waveney south and on the river Thyrn, north . . . in this vast tract of meadows are fed a prodigious number of black cattle which are said to be fed up for the fattest beef, though not the largest in England, and the quantity is so great as that they not only supply the City of Norwich, the town of Yarmouth, and county adjacent, but send great quantities of them weekly in all the winter season to London . . . And in this particular is worthy remark, that the gross of all the Scots cattle which come yearly into England, are brought hither, being brought to a small village lying north of the City of Norwich, called St. Faith's, where the Norfolk graziers go and buy them. These Scots runts, so they call them, coming out of the cold and barren mountains of the Highlands in Scotland, feed so eagerly on the rich pasture in these marshes that they thrive in an unusual manner and grow monstrously fat, and the beef is so delicious to taste that the inhabitants prefer them to the English cattle, which are much larger and fairer to look at, and they may very well do so. Some have told me, and I believe with good judgment, that there are about 40,000 of these Scots cattle fed in this country every year and most of them in the said marshes between Norwich, Beccles and Yarmouth.

The cycle of the grazing marshman's year thus started at the end of March, when the marshes were let by auction for the following twelve months. At the turn of this century a marsh farm, which might range typically from some twenty to a hundred acres, might be rented for £2 an acre, or perhaps £3 if it were on good grazing land. The cattle then had to be tended and the mills worked to keep the water low in the dykes, but with enough left for the cattle to drink and to prevent them from straying. By the beginning of November, all the cattle were off the marshes and the winter maintenance began. The marshman's first priority was then to clear the dykes of accumulated mud, reed and other growth, so as to minimize the seasonal inundation and ensure that the marshes were firm and well drained for the arrival of the cattle the following spring. This process, known as "dydling" or "deep drawing", entailed working the mill as hard as possible to keep the water level to a minimum and then damming a length of dyke and cleaning it out with a variety of tools. These differed from one locality to another, but a common one was the "dydle", a tool somewhat resembling an inverted dustpan mounted on a long pole, with which the mud was scraped from the bottom of the dyke. Another tool was the "cromb", also mounted on a pole, which carried three or four longish curved prongs with which undergrowth was cleared. To cut reeds under water, a short-bladed scythe called a "tuttle" was used, while the "crane-cutter" and "bar-cutter" were instruments, also with short blades, with which reeds and turf were cut from the banks of the dykes. Sometimes a "scoop" was used in place of the dydle: this was a wooden shovel tipped with iron, with a hollowed surface and a leather hood where the blade met the haft. All in all, "dydling a deek" was a wet, cold, hard and solitary occupation, but one that was essential for the drainage and preservation of the grazing marshes. Even more onerous was "bottomfying", the process—which speaks for itself —of redigging a badly overgrown dyke.

Something of the marshman's pattern of life can be discerned from the records of the old Ludham levels. These were enclosed at the end of the eighteenth century, at which time the Commissioners of Drainage concluded an agreement with a certain Edmund Rice for the working of two windpumps, one at Bridgefen, downstream from Ludham bridge, and the other at Horsefen, some distance away to the east beyond Womack Water. The contract, which was priced at £37 10s a year, also provided for the clearance of the dykes at the rate of 1s 3d a rod. As Edmund Rice was also a tenant grazier, his life must have been somewhat busy, particularly since both pumps had to be reefed and turned into the wind by hand. He apparently kept going for many years, however, until two of his sons took over a pump each. Several

A reed boat on the Broads.
Eastern Daily Press

generations of Rices worked these levels, and although a Ben Rice terminated the agreement in 1880 when the windpumps were replaced by steam mills, his son Bob was still working as a marshman, as well as operating the ferry and a turbine pumping mill at Thurne, at the time of the great flood of 1912. W. A. Dutt also tells of a marshman who had under his charge a windpump, four miles of dykes and frequently as many as two hundred head of cattle.

In the undrained areas of fen, other activities contributed to the marshman's livelihood. A main one was the cutting and sale of reed; this, with the thatching that went with it, was an important local industry over many centuries. One of the former "characters" of Broadland, "Thatcher" Grapes, believed that the craft had been handed down in his family for some six or seven hundred years. He himself started learning it at the age of nine and worked all his life on Woodbastwick and Ranworth Marshes; he did not retire until he was eighty-two. In Norwich, as elsewhere, the thatching profession was a fully recognized one and an enactment of 1665 has survived requiring a seven-year apprenticeship. The cutting of the reed began each year about Christmas time, as soon as the stems were dry and the leaves had fallen, and continued until the young reeds or "colts" emerged above the water in early April. Working from a boat or on the marsh itself, the marshmen usually

During the Reed Harvest. Possibly the best known of P. H. Emerson's photographs.

cut the reed with a scythe to the haft of which was fixed a hoop of osier known as a "byle". This hoop carried the reeds as they were cut and left them all lying one way, so that they could be easily gathered. Each bundle or "shofe" of reed was cleaned and tidied by combing it with an implement constructed from a piece of wood into which had been driven a row of long nails, and it was then tied with a reed bond. A bundle of five shofes measured six feet round at the height of the bond and was known as a "fathom", and the reeds were normally sold by the "long hundred" of 120 fathoms. It was possible for an expert to cut twenty fathoms in a day, but ten to fourteen was reckoned to be a good day's work—depending on the density of the reed, the thickness of the stems and the depth of the water. Once cut and bundled, the reeds would generally be transported in large, flat-bottomed "reedboats" to the nearest staithe, where they would be stacked, or "haled", in order to dry.

Other crops obtained from the fen included sedge, which—because it was less brittle than reed—was used to cover the ridges of reed-thatched houses, and "gladden", the lesser reedmace, which was used for horse collars and soft baskets. The true bulrush, or "bolder", was also made into horse collars, woven baskets (known as "frails") and rush mats, and was used by coopers as a seal between the staves of barrels. Rush-beds were generally cut every other year, between the end of June and the end of August. The bundles of rush were then stacked on dry land and turned carefully so that they weathered evenly and to a good condition and colour. As late as 1940 horse collars were still being made from bolder and gladden at Woods' in Ber Street, Norwich, a father-and-son business which also specialized in basket-making. Also in July and August, marsh hay of a high quality was regularly cut from the drained marshes, while the rougher growth from the less well-drained areas, often referred to as "schoof-stuff", made valuable litter. Both were sent to London in bulk for the use of cab-horses, while litter was also used for lining potato and beet clamps and for manure.

Peat continued to be dug after the inundation of the Broads, but only from shallow diggings known as "turf ponds". There are several records of peat digging in the Broads area in the early nineteenth century; for example, the Enclosure Act of 1818 mentions thirty-five acres of land at Neatishead and Catfield which were reserved for fuel. Later in the century, however, as the transport of coal improved, peat largely went out of use, although it was still being sold at Horning around 1900 at a shilling a hundred turves.

Osiers were also grown for basket- and hurdle-making, those from Surlingham being reckoned to be of a particularly good quality, and many Broadland farmers and marshmen cultivated their own osier beds. Broadland was an important centre of the craft, much of the output being "swills" for the Yarmouth fishing fleet. Skeps and baskets were also made for land work, as well as for carrying coal, malt and provisions generally.

The "harvest of the Broads" was not, however, confined to crops that could be gathered from the marshes. The wildlife was also shot, netted, snared or otherwise caught and killed, for sale away from Broadland as well as for local consumption. In 1542, the accounts of the city of Norwich show that in order to provide hospitality to the Duke of Norfolk, the City Fathers paid a "Mr Notyngham of Hycklyng" five shillings for a "pyper" (ie immature) crane and fourpence for bringing it to Norwich—a record, incidentally, which suggests that cranes were breeding in the Broads at that time. One of the most fascinating occupations was that of the eel-man, who traditionally caught his eels in large numbers and in a variety of ways for eventual sale not only in Norwich and Yarmouth but also as far afield as Billingsgate and the

Midlands. Until the early years of this century—not least in the Broads—little was known about the eel and there was a wealth of misconceptions about not only its breeding and migratory cycle but also whether there was more than one species. As we now know, there is in fact only one species of freshwater eel in Western Europe, differences in appearance being due to age and sex. For example, the male rarely grows beyond some twenty inches in length but the female may reach a length of three to four feet and weigh several pounds. These large females are extremely voracious and acquire a distinct appearance from the development of the jaw muscles, causing them to be classed in earlier times as a separate species, the broad-nosed eel. A distinction was also drawn between yellow eels (known in the Broads as "grigs") and silver eels, although the latter are merely eels that have changed their colour in preparation for the autumn migration to the sea. It was known from observation that only silver eels migrated to the sea, whence none ever returned, and that young elvers, normally about two and a half inches long, migrated up the rivers each spring. George Christopher Davies, writing in 1884, drew the obvious conclusion that spawning must take place at sea but was reluctant to believe that it did not also take place in the rivers, given that the eels clearly spent several years there as adults. As we now know, of course, the migration cycle of the eel is as remarkable as that of the salmon. Spawning takes place exclusively in the Sargasso Sea west of longitude 50°W, whence the eel larvae are carried across the Atlantic to shores as far apart as Iceland and the Mediterranean. The eels then stay in fresh water until they become sexually mature, which may take ten years or more in the case of a female. As they reach maturity, they start to migrate to the sea in late summer or autumn, reaching their spawning grounds the following spring and there procreating and dying.

One of the common ways of catching eels was by spearing them with an "eel-pick", a form of spear headed with four or five flat, flexible tines arranged slightly fanwise so that they would grip the eel rather than pierce it. A practised spearer would be able to locate the eels in the mud by means of their "blow-holes". Another means was by "bobbing" or "babbing". The technique was to thread a quantity of worms on a length of worsted, which was then looped into a bunch and tied to a line attached to a pole. The bunch was "bobbed" gently up and down in a few feet of water. An eel taking a worm was liable to catch its teeth in the worsted; then it could be raised to the surface and dropped into a convenient container. Lines were also laid for eels overnight, with perhaps as many as thirty or forty baited hooks attached to a single line.

The most rewarding way of catching eels, however, was by the use of eel-sets. Sets were to be found all over the Broads, although

Head of an eel pick. The maker was Robert Flaxman, reckoned to be the best manufacturer of picks of his day.
Norfolk Museums Service

Eel fisher's boat with pods.
Norfolk Library Services

those on Kendal Dyke, which caught the migration from the Hickling/Horsey area, were reckoned to be the most lucrative. They have a lengthy history, and there is a record of a sixteenth-century dispute with the bailiffs of Yarmouth over the grant of annual leases of no fewer than thirty-eight sets. Some sixty or seventy sets were said to be working in the early years of the nineteenth century. The management of an eel-set was a seasonal occupation, taking place during the autumn when the eels made their annual migration to the sea. A set consisted of an arrangement of close-meshed nets with floats at the top and weights at the bottom; this was stretched across the river along a row of stakes. To the stakes were attached ropes and blocks to enable the set to be pulled to the bottom of the river when any river craft was passing. At intervals along the nets were openings to netted funnels which led downstream and terminated in "pods" stretched on circular wicker hoops. Within the pods was also a series of funnels, allowing the eels to pass downstream but preventing their return. On encountering the set, the eels would find their way down the funnels to the "pods", which could be detached and drawn ashore to be emptied. As eels tend to run at night, the eel-man would spend the season by the set, often in a houseboat or an old sea boat, which, if it were too leaky, would be drawn up on the bank. When caught, the eels were kept in the river in "eel-boxes" until there were enough to send to market. Eels from the Bure were regularly despatched by train to Billingsgate, often packed in a stack of wooden trays topped by a tray full of ice so that water dripped on the eels while in transit and enabled them to reach the market alive. The price fetched at the end of the last century might vary between nine shillings and fourteen shillings a stone. The catches recorded from sets were often substantial: George Christopher Davies, for

Eel-set on the River Ant. F. G. Kitton

20

example, tells of a marshman who had caught three hundred stones of eels in four nights from a set at Hardley Cross on the Yare. The profits from a set might indeed have been enough to support the eel-man over the rest of the year.

Fishing was also a marshman's occupation, and the stories of commercial catches from the Broads are sometimes as difficult to credit as fishermen's tales anywhere. A turning point came in 1877, when as a result of pressures from the angling fraternity the passing of the Norfolk and Suffolk Fisheries Act led to the prohibition of drag-netting over most of the Broads. Prior to that time, the use of such nets, which might be up to a hundred yards long, had resulted in some prodigious catches of fish, which might be used as manure on the land if there were no ready sale for them. In more restricted waters bow nets or flue nets were used, the former being cylindrical nets set on hoops with a funnelled entrance at each end, while the latter were single or double layers of netting that would be set across narrow openings and the fish driven into them. Pike were highly valued and were often caught by the technique of liggering. Liggers were closely bound bundles of reeds about the size of a rolling-pin to which were attached two lengths of twine. One led to a lead weight and the other, after it had been wound securely round the ligger, to a strong double pike hook to which had been threaded a small live roach. Several liggers would be dropped from a boat at spots where the struggles of the baited roach would quickly attract carnivorous pike. It is on record that on one occasion as many as eighty pike were caught from liggers in a single day.

In former days there was a profitable trade in waterfowl, not merely for local markets but also for London. Prominent among the suppliers of these markets were the Breydoners—the fishermen, wildfowlers and punt gunners who fished and shot over Breydon Water and of whom little would be known but for the writings of Arthur Patterson. Over the years Breydon gradually lost the saltings and reed-beds which at one time surrounded large parts of it; meanwhile the silt deposited by the Yare and the Waveney built up the mudflats to the point where substantial areas that in the mid-nineteenth century had four feet or more of water at low tide were entirely dry fifty years later. According to Arthur Patterson, there were formerly some twenty or twenty-five professional punt gunners on Breydon, each with his own particular "pitch" and many of them living in crude shacks or houseboats along the shore. Punts varied slightly in shape and size across the Broads, but they were essentially a canoe type of small craft with a shallow displacement, pointed at both ends. The cockpit was long enough to hold the gun mounting and a man lying prone, and the punt could be sculled, paddled or quanted, or rigged with a small mast and sail. A punt gun was a formidable weapon, with a length of between six and nine feet and a bore of an inch and a half or more. It might weigh as much as a hundred pounds and be loaded with up to a pound of shot. Early punt guns were flintlocks, but later ones were fired with percussion caps. They were mounted on the punt by means of a thick iron pin which fitted into a socket in a heavy wooden cross-beam. Depending on the size of the gun, the mounting might include an arrangement of springs as a recoil mechanism. Boat and gun were often painted lead-grey, "the colour of the water". The gunner's technique was to lie in the punt and cautiously scull or paddle it towards any flock of wildflow resting on the mudbanks. When within range, he would kick on the floor of the punt and fire the gun as the startled fowl rose into the air. Recorded kills from a single discharge include one of eighty-three wildfowl and another of a hundred dunlins. Punt gunners were at one time also in evidence on Hickling, Barton and Rockland Broads. Injuries from faulty discharges were not uncommon.

One of the best known Breydoners was "Pintail" Thomas, who died in 1901 having spent, like his father and grandfather before him, the best part of a lifetime on Breydon Water. Arthur Patterson, who knew him for over thirty years, describes how as a boy in Yarmouth he had regarded Thomas's shop, where he sold the birds he had gunned or shot, as "a kind of wonderland", with "huge dishes . . . often full and piled with knots, turnstones, dunlin and ring plovers . . . Rows of gulls, ducks and curlews adorned the hooks outside." Patterson also describes Thomas's shooting of an osprey with his punt gun, for a profitable side-line for the gunners was the killing of species for the benefit of collectors of rare birds. One such collection of stuffed birds is to be seen in Norwich Castle Museum.

Another well-known Yarmouth game-dealer, by the name of Durrant, seems to have retailed an even larger range of birds than Thomas. Patterson reproduces Durrant's market book for 29th November, 1890, and records it as listing:

1 Bittern	110 Common Snipe
240 Dunlins	2 Bewick's Swans
9 Knots	1 Pintail
11 Woodcock	3 Curlew
47 Duck and Mallard	14 Jack Snipe
52 Blackbirds and Thrushes	Golden-Eye (various)
1 Godwit	39 Larks
14 Plovers (various)	

Patterson describes Durrant as having received from the gunners of Breydon most of the many thousands of birds which he sold. Yet another Yarmouth dealer was Isaac Harvey, who is recorded as having purchased nearly all the fowl that were brought into Yarmouth . . . He sent to London on an average fifty a week all through the season (this did not include those taken in decoys); sometimes the number was greatly exceeded, as in one week of 1829 when he had brought to him no less than four hundred wild fowl of different descriptions, five hundred snipe and one hundred and fifty golden plover, all of which found a ready sale in London. In the summer this man also sent to London between six hundred and seven hundred eggs weekly . . . Thus, the eggs taken and the birds destroyed, the inevitable result was that many species rapidly decreased in numbers and finally became extinct.

Durrant's Game Shop at Yarmouth in 1900. On the left, talking to Durrant, is Arthur Patterson.
Norfolk Library Services

In time, the imposition of a close season, together with the deterioration and increased use of Breydon, put paid to the trade in wildfowl and waders. The gunners turned their attention to the catching of eels and a variety of fish. They speared or babbed for eels and laid eel-pots, and fished for smelts with a close-meshed net which was laid in a wide semicircle and then dragged ashore. The last of the Breydon wildfowlers is said to have been one "Diamond" Allen, who died in Yarmouth in 1963 at the age of eighty-four, one of the few who were still making a living on Breydon in the nineteen-thirties. By that time much of their income was derived from guiding "gentlemen wildfowlers", since the numbers of wildfowl had greatly decreased. But eels could still be caught and would find a ready market in the summer at a shilling a pound, while smelts were also in demand at 1s 9d to two shillings a score.

A few miles inland from Breydon lies Rockland Broad, an expanse of water and fen about 120 acres in extent, lying at the end of a dyke on the south bank of the Yare. One of the most beautiful of the Broads, this was the stamping ground of "Scientific" Fuller, one of the last and most notorious of the marshmen, who spent some sixty years making a living there. Described by James Wentworth Day as a "splendid, smelly, lovable old man . . . short, bearded and broad-shouldered with fierce eyes, wild hair and wilder whiskers", he lived on a houseboat on the Broad, which he plundered with his punt gun, fowling pieces, liggers, nets, eel-pick and eel-pots. He too kept an eye wide open for the rarer species of bird, which he sold to the "gentlemen collectors".

The wildfowl market was also supplied by the use of decoys. The principles of a duck decoy were extremely simple. It consisted of a netted corridor or "pipe" erected over an inlet to a lake. The net was spread over a series of iron hoops, tapering from some eighteen feet in width at the entrance to a small exit at the far extremity to which was attached a cylindrical net stretched on hoops, very much on the principle of the eel-man's "pod". The whole decoy would perhaps be some eighty or ninety yards long and would be set in a curve so that the end was not visible from the

*A duck decoy.
Illustration to an article
by G. Christopher Davies,
written in 1882.*

entrance. On each side of the decoy there were overlapping rush screens, each large enough to conceal a man from the view of the ducks in the "pipe". The ideal was to set a number of decoys round a lake, since decoys could only be worked when upwind from the wildfowl (decoys were never used in rivers).

The key to the effectiveness of the decoy is that ducks are, for some reason, attracted by dogs. One theory is that they mistake a dog for a fox. Because they are preyed on by foxes when roosting on land they become highly excited when they see one, and as long as they are on water and believe themselves safe they will pursue what they think is a fox whenever one comes into view. A theory that is perhaps more probable is that ducks are inquisitive creatures and are attracted by anything that moves. However that may be, the appearance of a dog from behind the screens would always attract ducks. When they were well into the decoy, the decoy-man would emerge from behind the screens at its mouth and panic the ducks into the net at the inner end, where they were caught and killed.

The decoy is said to have been introduced into Norfolk by Sir William Wodehouse, the Lord of Waxham Manor, in the reign of James I; Sir Thomas Browne, writing in the middle of the seventeenth century, talks of "the very many decoys, especially between Norwich and the sea". Evidence of their location often remains in the form of place-names—Decoy Broad in the Woodbastwick Marshes, Decoy Farm on Ormesby Broad, Decoy Covert near Waxham and Fritton Decoy behind Lowestoft, to name a few. There seem to have been some ten to twelve still in existence in the early nineteenth century. They progressively went out of use as wildfowling became more prevalent, since the key requirement for a decoy was a wholly undisturbed lake where the duck could feel themselves safe. It is on record that in the nineteenth century a ton and a half of fowl from one decoy were sent to London four times a week, netting the decoy-man £1,000 in the season. In Norfolk as a whole, it is reckoned that in the heyday of the decoy in the eighteenth century there may have been as many as a hundred decoys operating, each taking on average five thousand birds in a season—which adds up to the remarkable figure of a half a million in all.

If one had to characterize in a single word the traditional way of life of the people of the Broadland marshes and villages, that word would be "self-reliance". It is true that in the primitive sense of the term they ran a market economy, in that they sold their labour, produce and artefacts, often over long distances, and in return purchased many of the necessities of everyday life. But most villages of any size had a variety of trades within their community —perhaps their own blacksmith, carpenter, builder, harness-maker, tailor, shoe-maker, thatcher, corn merchant and all-purpose shop. The sense of community was also enhanced by the church, chapel and public house. Often there were small industries: brick-making, milling, malting, brewing or boat-building. Many villagers built their own cottages from wattle, daub and thatch. Most cottagers would have their own pig, chickens and fruit and vegetables. Peat could often be cut from the Poors' Fens, the commons set aside to provide for the needier villagers. Fish, wildfowl and rabbits were at hand for catching or shooting. Poaching was by no means ruled out. It was only with the improvement of communications with the outside world and the immense increase in mobility of people and goods that the traditional Broads economy began to break down.

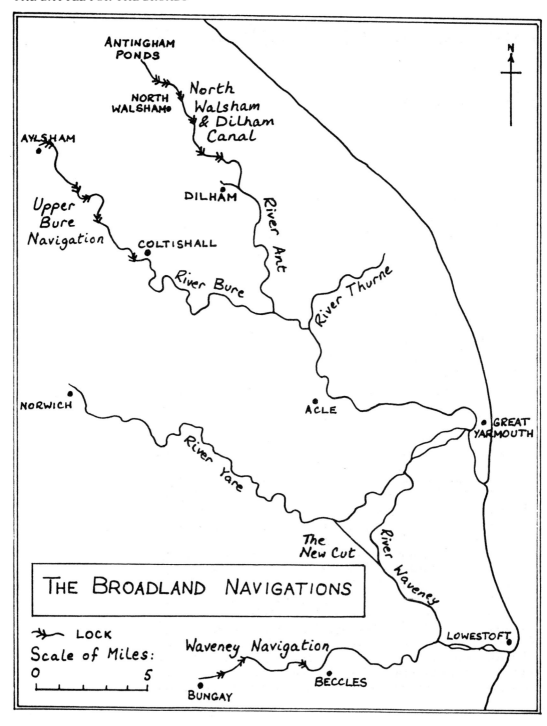

ANTINGHAM PONDS

NORTH WALSHAM

North Walsham & Dilham Canal

AYLSHAM

DILHAM

Upper Bure Navigation

River Ant

COLTISHALL

River Bure

River Thurne

NORWICH

ACLE

GREAT YARMOUTH

River Yare

The New Cut

River Waveney

LOWESTOFT

THE BROADLAND NAVIGATIONS

LOCK

Scale of Miles:

0   5

Waveney Navigation

BUNGAY

BECCLES

The Traditional Life of Broadland: the Waterways   3

Norwich adds greatly to the trade of Yarmouth, by the importation of about 40,000 chaldrons of coals yearly; wine, fish, oil, Irish yarn and all heavy goods, which come from thence by the River Yare: and in peace the exportation of its manufactures to Russia, Germany, Holland, Denmark, Norway, Spain, Portugal, Italy, etc. . . . The keels and wherries which navigate between Norwich and Yarmouth are acknowledged to be superior to any other small craft in England, for carrying a larger burthen and being worked at smaller expense:– their burthen is from fifteen to fifty tons; they have but one mast, which lets down, and carry only one square sail, are covered by hatches, and have a cabin superior to many coasting vessels, in which oftentimes the keelman and his family live; they require only two persons to navigate them, and sometimes perform their passage (of thirty-two miles) in five hours.

A Concise History and Directory of the City of Norwich for 1810

Just as the traditional Broadland enterprises were not simply local in scope but had commercial linkages as far afield as London and Scotland, so the commercial traffic on the Yare, Waveney and Bure has from earliest times made a significant contribution to the economy of the region, both internally and in facilitating national and international trade. The Romans built roads into the area, including Pye Road—the highway that led from Colchester to Caistor St Edmund—and, less certainly, the road later known as Fincham Drove, which may have connected Caister-on-Sea to the Midlands via Wayford Bridge. But there is little doubt that the Romans relied on the Broadlands rivers for much of their internal transportation; it is very probable that Caistor St Edmund is sited where it is, on the River Tas, because of its easy communications by water to Caister-on-Sea and beyond. Over most of the subsequent centuries, roads in the area remained rudimentary and unreliable, and navigation along the rivers was a much easier and more economical form of transport. For several months of the year many roads, particularly in the low-lying areas, became wholly impassable to wheeled traffic. As recently as a century ago, for examples, bundles of brushwood and reed had to be laid in order to prevent wagons from being bogged down on the track between Somerton and Horsey. Conditions became a little easier, particularly for passenger traffic, with the coming of the turnpikes in the eighteenth century. However, up to the time of the building of the railways in the mid-nineteenth century what was known as the "Norwich Navigation"—linking that city with Yarmouth along the Rivers Wensum and Yare—was of the first importance to the economic growth of both, while most Broadland towns and villages relied on the rivers for the delivery and despatch of produce of any weight or bulk.

Norwich was already a substantial settlement in Anglo-Saxon times. Although it received a setback following the Norman invasion, by the middle of the fourteenth century it had become the sixth richest city in England, its wealth relying primarily on the wool trade. Much of the trade was generated in the Norfolk villages, including several just north and west of Broadland proper—the village of Worstead, for example, with its great "wool church", is famous for the cloth of that name—but weaving was a major Norwich industry, and both wool and cloth were exported through Yarmouth in substantial quantities. In the late fourteenth century Yarmouth was the entrepot for three quarters of the worsted cloth produced in the county. By the sixteenth century, with agriculture as well as its own cloth industry thriving, Norwich was a leading commercial centre. Yarmouth Quay was by then the second largest port in Europe, its prosperity solidly based on the cargoes that had to be transshipped between the river craft which plied to and from Norwich and the sea-going vessels that sailed to the Continent and even to the Mediterranean. It is not surprising that disputes arose over the navigation and the terms of trade between the two, but recognition of their common interests eventually prevailed. In 1543 a cross was erected near Hardley, where the River Chet meets the Yare, to mark the boundary between the two navigational jurisdictions. Annually thereafter, a joint civic meeting was held at Hardley Cross to settle any differences which had arisen during the previous year and to confirm and celebrate the relationship.

In the course of the sixteenth century the Norfolk weaving industry suffered something of a decline. However, fresh impetus was imparted by the arrival towards the end of the century of large numbers of Dutch weavers who had fled as refugees following the bloody suppression of their revolt against their Spanish overlords. A population explosion took place in the seventeenth century and by the beginning of the eighteenth Norwich was the largest provincial city in the land. There was a great increase in the demand for woollen goods, while agriculture and trade and industry in general prospered as never before. By the end of the century Norwich was exporting textiles as far afield as India and China and receiving luxury goods in return, while Norfolk was exporting more grain than the rest of England put together. It was not until the Napoleonic Wars had gravely damaged her foreign trade and her weavers were meeting increasing competition from the growing textile industry of northern England that Norwich's slow decline—and with it the decline of the main river traffic—began.

Perhaps as a result of a sense of frustration at this reversal of fortunes, relations between Norwich and Yarmouth again deteriorated. Irked by the inconvenience and costs of transshipment, in the early nineteenth century the Norwich authorities launched what was known as the "Norwich a Port" campaign. The aim was to enable sea-going vessels to bypass Yarmouth and sail up to Norwich via an enlarged port and locks at Lowestoft and a channel, the "New Cut", between the Waveney and the Yare. Fierce opposition from Yarmouth ensued and the first Lowestoft Navigation Bill was defeated in Parliament in 1825, much to the delight of the Yarmouth burgesses, who held a dinner to celebrate. But their satisfaction was short-lived: a second Bill was passed in 1827.

The New Cut. This channel was opened in 1833 in order to give Norwich access to the sea through Lowestoft. Despite the pylons, the New Cut runs between Grade I and Grade II grazing marsh.
P. A. Ewans

In 1833 the passage from Lowestoft, with a minimum depth of ten feet all the way to Norwich, was formally opened amid scenes of jubilation when two steamboats, the *Squire* and the *City of Norwich*, arrived in the city. The project was, however, never much of a success. It could only accommodate the smaller end of the range of sea-going ships; the Yarmouth authorities promptly reduced their dues in order to compete; and the age of the train soon intervened, Norwich and Yarmouth being connected by rail in 1844. Eventually, the more sensible solution of dredging the channel from Yarmouth was adopted, and Norwich has continued in a modest way as a port for British and foreign coasting vessels. Its heyday was between the two world wars, when a new Haven Bridge was constructed at Yarmouth and a new Carrow Bridge and turning basin for ships at Norwich. A good deal of dredging and piling was also undertaken on the Yare. In the decade between the mid-twenties and the mid-thirties river traffic on the Yare increased some fivefold and in the nineteen-thirties some thirty to forty thousand tons of coal were being delivered by water to the city each year. In 1938 735 ships docked in the city, their cargoes including coal, grain, bricks, tiles, paper and timber, and as many as five hundred were still arriving in the nineteen-sixties. The trade fell

"Norwich a Port." An advertisement of a direct London–Norwich freight service, following the opening of the Lowestoft–Norwich Navigation in 1833.
Norfolk Library Services

NORWICH A PORT.

LONDON TRADERS.

REDUCED FREIGHTS.

LONDON, LOWESTOFT, AND NORWICH SHIPPING COMPANY.

A REGULAR LINE OF VESSELS IS NOW ESTABLISHED FROM

GRIFFIN'S WHARF, LONDON,

TO NORWICH DIRECT;

And, to prevent delay, a STEAM TUG of 27-Horse Power has been engaged.

VESSELS will Load every WEDNESDAY, at GRIFFIN'S WHARF, and at R. and S. RUDRUM'S WHARF, every THURSDAY. The Committee of the above Company respectfully invite the Shippers of Norwich to support this undertaking, and they beg to announce that it is their intention to Start TWO Vessels from each end every Week.   (4547

For Freight apply to R. and S. RUDRUM, *King Street, Norwich,*
W. V. BARNARD, *Lowestoft,*
THOS. FARNCOMB, *Griffin's Wharf, London,*

Norwich, 1st October, 1833.   AGENTS TO THE COMPANY.

off substantially when the gasworks was converted from coal and part of the electricity generating station from coal to diesel. Beccles was also opened to sea-going trade in the eighteen-thirties, and as late as 1932 six cargo vessels—two of them sailing barges—arrived with cargoes of barley, which they had collected from a Canadian ship in the Thames for the local maltings.

In the seventeenth and eighteenth centuries, as commerce grew and the advantages of transporting goods by river became increasingly apparent, thoughts turned to the possibility of canalizing the upper reaches of the Broads rivers. There were even ideas of cutting a canal through to the Ouse: a route via the Waveney and the Little Ouse was suggested in 1652 and a route from Norwich in 1777, via Wymondham, Hingham, Watton and Stoke Ferry. The Waveney is said to have been navigable as far as Bungay in quite early times, but if so the navigation at some point ceased and an Act was passed in 1670 in order to reopen it. Locks were constructed at Geldeston, Ellingham and Wainford; the river was dredged; and the navigation appears to have brought a good deal of prosperity to Bungay and surrounding parts. It survived until 1934, when the locks finally fell into disuse. Alysham and North Walsham were two more towns which saw the advantages of substituting water transport for the expense and unreliability of the road system. The Bure from Coltishall to Aylsham became a navigable waterway by an Act of 1773, and after problems with contractors who overran their estimates and subscribers who defaulted on their payments the navigation eventually came into use in 1779. There were five locks on the route, which was used extensively for many years, and by 1834 a regular weekly wherry service was running from Aylsham to Yarmouth. Even after the opening of the railway between Norwich and Aylsham in 1874 the river was regularly used by some thirty wherries. The navigation was finally closed after the floods of 1912 carried away the lock at Buxton Mills.

Contemporary records tell us rather more about the North Walsham and Dilham Canal, which was opened in 1826. The project was first mooted in 1811, amid expressions of extreme dissatisfaction at the cost of carrying goods to North Walsham along the turnpike from the then head of navigation at Dilham. It was not for another twelve years that the necessary Act was passed and work began. A large contingent of "bankers" from Bedford-shire, who were employed for the purpose, marched out of North Walsham on 5 April, 1825

in regular order, proceeded [sic] by the committee, with colours flying and a band of music, to Austin Bridge, where the first spade of earth was cut . . . After the men had worked for a few minutes they returned

A Norfolk Wherry.

to the market in the same order to partake of some barrels of strong beer, which were gratuitously distributed among them.

A proper concern for priorities was also observed for the ceremonies marking the arrival of the first wherries at North Walsham a little over a year later. Flags and music were again in evidence, and the day finished with "a plentiful treat to the workmen of Mr Sharpe's strong ale and Barclay's brown stout". When the whole canal was formally opened in August, 1826, a fleet of vessels sailed through its seven locks, with upwards of a thousand persons afloat and the banks of the canal thronged with "all the fashion and beauty of the neighbourhood, highly delighted with the novelty of the scene". Having reached the head of navigation, the whole company returned in procession to North Walsham and a dinner was held at the King's Arms, hosted by the Lord Lieutenant of the County and Lord Suffield, the owner of nearby Gunton Hall, after which interminable toasts were proposed and replied to, and "conviviality prevailed to a late hour". For all this self-congratulation, however, the canal had major drawbacks in that there was not enough water in Antingham Ponds, at its head, to fill the locks more than three times a day and its dimensions limited passage to small wherries. It was only with extreme difficulty that the writer and photographer P. H. Emerson (of whom more later) managed in 1891 to penetrate to Antingham Ponds in his converted wherry, *Maid of the Mist*, and for many years the head of navigation reached no further than North Walsham. The whole navigation finally fell into disuse in 1935.

The earliest trading vessels plying the Broads about which anything is known are the Norfolk keels. According to Frank Carr, keelmen appear as a Norwich guild in 1533, while the earliest record of an actual keel dates from 1561 when one was offered for sale at Buckenham Ferry at a price of £60. However, it is by no means fanciful to see them, with their long hulls and square rigs, as descendants of the Viking longships, as indeed were many of the medieval trading vessels of Western Europe. The keel was a clinker-built craft with a single mast stepped amidships which could be raised and lowered by a forestay operated by a winch at the bows. Its square sail was set on a yard which was hoisted by another winch at the stern and trimmed by sheets leading aft to the helmsman. The hold covered much of the length of the craft, but there was a small cabin in the bows. A deck or plankway ran each side of the hold; from it the keel could be poled or "quanted" when the wind was absent or adverse. The last surviving keel, which had been used for carrying timber until 1890, was sunk at Postwick to help reinforce the river bank but was partially excavated in 1912 so that measurements could be taken. It was found that she was fifty-five feet in length, 13 feet 8 inches in beam and four feet in depth, and was probably capable of carrying a load of some thirty tons. There is some evidence that earlier keels had pointed sterns but this one, like most of the later ones, had a small transom. She has now been salvaged and is being preserved in Norwich.

The keel's square rig was of course a major disadvantage, especially on the winding Broads rivers, and it is painful to think of the amount of quanting which keelmen must have had to undertake whenever a head wind was encountered. It is therefore no wonder that the keels were gradually superseded by the wherries. These, with their fore and aft rigs, were vastly superior sailing machines. Again, it is not known when or by whom the Norfolk wherry was invented, but it is a reasonable supposition that the first wherries dated from the late sixteenth century and the arrival of the Dutch refugees. It can be safely assumed that the ships in which they came had fore and aft rigs, which were at that time well developed on the Continent but had not yet been adopted in England. A plan of Yarmouth dating from about 1580 shows for the first time vessels with unmistakable fore and aft rigs and suggests a marriage between this rig and the traditional longboat hull. Wherries of one sort or another were already in existence on the Thames and elsewhere, the word being used to describe a boat which carried passengers—whether driven by oars or by sail—and it seems likely that the first Norfolk wherries were also passenger-carrying craft, with the advantage of being able to beat the keels hands down when speed was important. Support for this theory is provided by a regulation issued by the burgesses of Norwich in 1616 that not only draws a clear distinction between "kelemen, wherrymen and boatemen" but also specifies wherries alone when referring to the "passage and repassage of merchants, factors and other persons to and from this Citty". But the exact timing and manner in which the wherries were developed remain a matter for speculation. The first drawing of a wherry-type vessel appears, along with several keels, in Buck's *South-east Prospect of Norwich*, which was published in 1741, while more precise evidence is provided by a horn cup dated 1789, now in Norwich Castle Museum, on which there is an unmistakable drawing of a wherry. An inscription on the cup reads "Success to the Happy Return", which must have been the wherry's name. It is likely that from small-scale beginnings, with a capacity of perhaps as little as five tons, the wherries progressively increased in size until they were able to carry cargoes of a weight to enable them to compete comprehensively with the keels and eventually drive them off Broadland rivers altogether. By the end of the eighteenth century 120 wherries were registered against thirty-six keels; and there-after, as they continued to increase in size, the wherries became

The 'Happy Return' Cup. Dated 1789, this horn cup, which was no doubt presented to mark the launching of the Happy Return, *carries an unmistakable drawing of a wherry.*
Norfolk Museums Service

supreme. By the middle of the nineteenth century over three hundred were estimated to be sailing on the Broads, the largest of them, the *Wonder*, of some eighty tons burden. The smallest, *Little Georgie*, of about five tons, was nicknamed the "Cabbage Wherry" because it was owned by a market gardener at Ludham and used by him to transport produce to Yarmouth market. Most wherries ranged between twenty and fifty tons.

The wherry differed from the keel in that the mast was stepped well forward, pivoting in a tabernacle in the bows, in order to accommodate the fore and aft rig. It was unstayed, apart from a forestay, and was counterbalanced by a substantial iron or lead weight, which meant that it was a simple task for a single person to lower and raise it by means of a tackle at the bows. It was thus not difficult for a wherry to lower its sail and mast, shoot a bridge and raise mast and sail again, the whole operation being carried out without losing steerage way. The wherry's immense single sail was carried on a high gaff and could be sheeted well in, which meant that the craft had an exceptional ability to sail into the wind. There was no boom, and a "bonnet" could be added to the foot of the sail to give it extra area in light winds. An ingenious arrangement of blocks enabled both throat and peak of the gaff to be hoisted on a single halliard operated from a winch in front of the mast. Most of the hull aft of the mast was taken up by the hold, apart from a small cabin in the stern and a well from which the craft could be operated. As in the keel, a plankway led down each side of the hull so that the vessel could be quanted, and the absence of shrouds meant that the quanter had an uninterrupted walk from bow to stern. As well as the rig, the wherry's hull was a major design accomplishment. It combined the roominess needed for carrying cargo with a shape that contributed to its exceptional sailing performance. Its draught had to be shallow to enable it to penetrate to the far reaches of the Broads rivers and dykes, but the flat sections amidships which this entailed gave way to pronounced flares at bow and stern. The hull design was such that it could be readily sailed when fully loaded, and the wherry retained its remarkable sailing abilities even when the water came over the gunwales or "bins". The flare at the bows also assisted the wherry in pointing along a lee shore, pushing a cushion of water against the bank and preventing it from making leeway, another design factor giving it exceptional performance on the narrow Broads rivers. It was said that as long as it retained steerage way it was well-nigh impossible to run a wherry aground to leeward. A further refinement was a slipping keel which was large enough to do away with the need for leeboards but could be unbolted in very shallow waters and refastened when the depth of water again permitted. Even the largest wherries could be operated by two persons, often the wherryman and his wife, and some were even sailed single-handed. The Norfolk wherry thus represented a remarkable combination of utility and grace, and it is one of the classic sailing craft designs, perfectly suited to the environment in which it worked.

The appearance of the wherry was no less remarkable than its sailing qualities. The hull was usually tarred black, while the sail—once it had been stretched—was painted with a mixture of coal tar, lamp-black and herring oil, a combination which left it nearly as black as the hull. The wherrymen were as keen as canal bargees to decorate their vessels: the hatch covers and cabin tops

Sail plan of the wherry Maud.

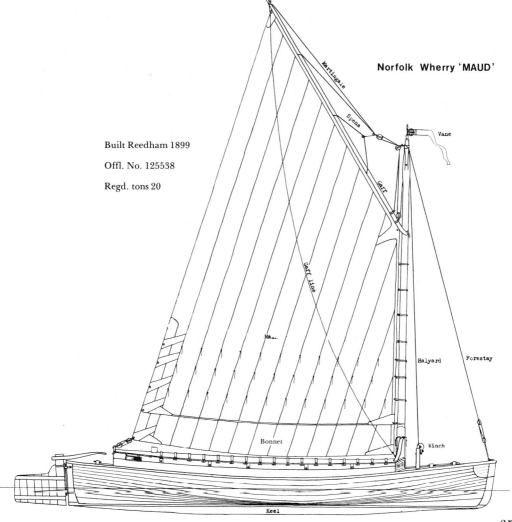

Norfolk Wherry 'MAUD'

Built Reedham 1899

Offl. No. 125538

Regd. tons 20

were often painted red, the uprights between deck and hatch covers white or blue, and many of the fittings were picked out in bright colours. The mast, of pitch- or Oregon pine, was oiled with linseed, accentuating its natural colour. The top five feet or so were painted with the colours of its owner, normally a band or bands of colour a few inches wide surmounted by a plain colour for the final three or four feet. A wherry could thus be identified when the masthead appeared over trees or buildings, before the vessel came fully into view. Perhaps the most unusual feature was the vane, which consisted of a metal plate to which a length of red bunting was attached. The plate was often decorated, while a "cut-out" of a figure was sometimes attached in front of the spindle. The most popular figure was a "Jenny Morgan", a silhouette of a Welsh girl with flared skirt and flowerpot flourishing a bunch of leeks. Vanes with figures came to be known generally as Jenny Morgans. The name was apparently taken from a popular song of the mid-nineteenth century. Finally, many wherries had a white quadrant painted on each side of their bows. There has been no little speculation about its origin and significance, but it is very likely that its purpose was simply to signal the approach of a wherry at night; they never carried lights since that would have adversely affected the wherryman's eyesight in the darkness.

The men responsible for the construction of the wherries were local craftsmen working out of small boatyards across Broadland. Two of the best known were Hall's of Reedham and Allen's of Coltishall. Perhaps the most famous wherry builder was William Brighton, who built the *Albion*, the last survivor of the trading wherries, at Oulton Broad in 1898. This wherry is still maintained and sailed by the Norfolk Wherry Trust. Many small yards also existed, producing a single wherry from time to time and doing repair and refitting work in the meanwhile. Coltishall is said to have been a boat-building centre for many centuries and the Anchor Street boatyard, behind the Anchor Inn, may have been operating in the sixteenth century or even earlier. In 1864 there was a major boatyard there which was bought at auction by one John Allen and remained in the family until the site was sold in 1974. The yard produced an average of one wherry a year until about 1900, but it turned towards wherry yachts in the eighteen-nineties and later built cruisers and carried out repair work. Allen's wherries were mainly built for the Ant and Bure, and were long, slender and comparatively light in design. The *Ella*, reputed to be the smallest and fastest, was designed in 1912 for the North Walsham–Dilham canal and was the last trading wherry to be built on the Broads.

The wherry builders used no plans or blueprints, but worked largely by eye, often following a family tradition. Many months of

Allen's Boatyard, Coltishall.

hard and heavy work were needed to build a wherry. The wood, normally found locally, would be selected with care, cut into planking with a two-handled saw in a saw-pit and seasoned. Smoothing or planing was done with an adze and holes were bored with an auger. Curved branches were also carefully selected to serve as shaped timbers; where a plank had to be bent to fit the curve of a wherry's hull it would be wetted, bent over an iron bar and heated at a fire of rushes and oak chips. Metal fittings would be bought in from a local blacksmith, while the sail usually came from a firm at Yarmouth. In the eighteen-eighties an average wherry of thirty tons might cost about £400 to build, and the eighty-ton *Wonder* is said to have cost about £1000.

The cargoes which the wherries carried comprised almost everything needed or traded locally, as well as imports from wider afield and exports of the region's produce and manufactures. In terms of local needs, the wherries' main standby was coal, which they delivered from Yarmouth to staithes over the length and breadth of the Broads, each of which might serve an appreciable area round about. Coal was also used for brick-kilns and steam drainage mills. Farmers relied heavily on wherries not only for the transport of their crops, including grain and sugar beet, but also for the inputs they needed, such as manure, fertilizer, cattle cake and marl. In the eighteenth and nineteenth centuries marl was widely used for improving land, and as carriage by wherry was comparatively cheap a substantial trade in it existed around Broadland. Much of it was quarried in an area south of the Bure between Coltishall and Wroxham which came to be known as Little Switzerland and to which the wherries penetrated through a network of narrow dykes. Mills were also built on the upper Broads rivers, not only to take advantage of the water power available but also because wherries could carry the corn they needed and the flour they produced to and from their doorsteps. At one time nearly all the coal merchants and corn and flour mills possessed wherries, but they were often assisted by independent wherrymen sailing their own craft. Another thriving Broadland industry, particularly in the nineteenth century, was malting. Excellent malting barley was grown in the area and wherries carried the malt not only to local breweries but also to Yarmouth for shipment to London and even to Ireland and the Netherlands. Many Broadland villages had their own small maltings, while Coltishall in the eighteen-eighties had eighteen malthouses, and up to twenty wherries sailed from the village each day during the malting season.

The local construction industry also depended extensively on the wherries. Small brick-kilns were built in places convenient to the rivers. Yarmouth, for example, was built largely with bricks carried to it from inland. It is said that at one time there were eleven brick-fields along the Broadlands rivers and that a freight of bricks was always readily available to the wherries. One of them, the *Martham Trader*, was more popularly known as the "Brick Hod". There were also cement works at Berney Mills and near Burgh Castle, the materials for which, including chalk from Norwich, came by water. The windpump at Berney Arms was at one stage used for grinding clinker for cement, while the well-known public house there, built in the seventeenth century, catered to the wherrymen on passage, as did many of the Broadland inns. Timber and reeds were other common cargoes and were to be seen stacked well above the wherries' holds. The wherrymen were in fact happy to carry any cargoes that were offered. In 1822 they were noted as carrying to Norwich cargoes of coal, groceries, ironmongery, timber, wine and spirits. In the eighteen-eighties house coal was carried from Yarmouth to Norwich for 1s 8d a ton and gas coal for 1s 4d, the average cargo for a thirty-ton wherry running to about £3. The dues levied by the Great Yarmouth Port and Haven Commissioners were set at a penny a ton. In winter, the

Opposite:
Above left: *Fen orchid* (Liparis loeselii).
Ivan West
Above right: *Yellow flag.* Broads Authority
Below: *Swallowtail butterfly* (Papilio madraon).
Ivan West

wherries collected ice from the broads, using a wire scoop on a long pole known as a "dydle", for carriage to Yarmouth for the herring industry. If sold direct to the fishing smacks ice might fetch as much as fifteen shillings a ton, but the trade was eventually undercut by ice carried from Norway. Many wherries also acted as lighters for ships too large to sail into Yarmouth, the *Wonder* being built specifically for this purpose. Among more unusual tasks, wherries carried bones to an artificial fertilizer factory at Antingham and acted as hearses, while the *Rob Roy*—alias the "Market Wherry"—carried market women twice a week from Reedham to Yarmouth, where they sold vegetables and farm produce. In 1957 eight wherries made the passage to the Solent, where they spent a year or more ferrying building materials for the construction of a barracks at Gosport.

The wherrymen themselves are often portrayed as hard-sailing, hard-drinking, hard-bitten characters, all too prone to schedule their passages from one riverside inn to another and not above a bit of smuggling or other nefarious activity when the opportunity arose. The Norwich burgesses of 1616 certainly seem to have taken this view—a regulation which they produced laid it down that since

> there ys nowe growen greate prophanacion of the Saboth to the high displeasure of Almighty God and many deceits and falsehoods are dayly practized by the kelemen wherrymen and other boatemen usinge passage and cariage upon the said Ryver and much idleness and lewdnes . . . no kele wherry or boate shall be used upon the Ryver within the liberties of this Citty upon any Saboth day . . . [and] . . . no keleman wherryman or other waterman . . . shall willingly or wittingly cary or suffer to passe in any of their keles wherryes or boates any common Rogue, harlott or ffelon.

(The fine imposed for sailing on the Sabbath was 4s 4d, and for carrying rogues etc ten shillings.) Certainly there was a fair amount of pilferage on the wherries. For example, a case is recorded in 1830 in which a wherryman and the owner of a waterside inn removed the hoops from four pipes of port which were in transit from Yarmouth, drilled holes in them, extracted about three gallons of wine from each pipe and watered down the remainder. Although they then plugged the holes and drove back the hoops to conceal them, the crime was discovered and each was sentenced to fourteen years' transportation.

Wherries proved handy in conveying goods inland after they had been landed illicitly somewhere on the deserted coastline north of Yarmouth. There was also a route from Crazy Mary's Hole, a gap in the cliffs between Pakefield and Kessingland south of Lowestoft, whence goods would be carted to the Waveney for carriage by wherry to Norwich. Favourite items seem to have been

Opposite:
The Thurne in summer.
Martin Trelawney

A wherry close-hauled. The wherry Albion *shows her paces on Breydon Water.*
Eastern Daily Press

tobacco, spirits, tea, silks and—on account of the tax on it—salt. The fact that the penalty for smuggling could include transportation seems not to have been much of a deterrent. Reedstacks and windpumps often proved useful temporary hiding places, and there was said to be a system of signalling by the positioning of the windpumps' sails to warn smugglers if excisemen were approaching. Berney Arms and the Chequers Inn at St Benet's were apparently important points on the smuggling routes. Wherries were also useful for illegal sports, such as cock-fighting and prize fights, since they could carry spectators to remote spots as well as provide a convenient means of escape if the law should appear over the horizon. They were occasionally used at election time for "cooping", that is as places of detention for the opposition's supporters. A case in 1833 entailed incarceration on a wherry on Ranworth Broad.

The wherrymen came in all sorts and conditions, as in most walks of life. Ted Beals of Hickling, who owned the *Emily*, may have been an exception, but he never sailed on a Sunday and walked to the nearest church for morning service from wherever he was moored. The wherrymen's work was onerous and by no means overpaid considering their skills and responsibilities. Wherry owners were reckoned to be men of substance, for their share of the profits amounted to what was regarded as a comfortable income. Those who sailed them might be paid by the voyage, a typical wage in the late nineteenth century for a passage between Norwich and Yarmouth being thirty shillings, or they might receive seven pence in the shilling of the total freightage, the payment being shared between the two members of the crew. They were afloat in most weathers, summer and winter alike. They were self-reliant, yet with a great sense of camaraderie. Above all, they took immense pride in their vessels and in their professional competence. For perhaps some three centuries the wherry, along with the windpump, gave the Broadland landscape much of its distinctive character, the two of them yielding only with the advent of steam and the internal combustion engine. In the case of the wherry, the death-knell was sounded first by the railway, then by the use of tugs with lighters and shallow-draught sea-going vessels which could sail right through to Norwich, and finally by the motor lorry. By the end of the First World War there were few trading wherries left, and they had all gone by the end of the Second. Let the last word on this vanished era lie with Arthur Patterson:

The Wherries' Graveyard: the remains of wherries sunk in Ranworth Broad in order to protect the bank. It was from Ranworth that the wherry Maud *was salvaged for restoration.*
M. K. Ewans

> In my youth it was an inspiring sight, watching from the old bowling green at Breydon Corner perhaps thirty, once thirty-six, wherries bowling off on the evening flood tide, here and there the pale blue smoke curling athwart the dark sails, as the old lady in the cabin got tea on the way, or perhaps a bloater; and then the craft, according to weights of cargo, forging ahead of each other until a long "trapseing" of sails disappeared round the Burgh bend, vanishing in the blue. Those restful days held the romance which we have lost today.

★　★　★

The Broadland Naturalists

4

Sunrise over the fen on these autumn mornings brings transient splendour to a realm of dew-wet reeds and a lingering cloak of mist. Through a haze of rose which turns to gold, countless geometric webs of spiders bridge darkling gaps, glittering and opalescent. Spear-leaves and drooping purple reed-plumes are beaded with silver and the pin-cushion umbels of angelica are pricked out with a million diamond points of light.

Tassels of hemp agrimony and magenta spires of loosestrife achieve a brightness and perfection which beautifies them, while white bellbines shine with the pallor of fading stars through the morning vapours. There is a scent of water mint distilled from the night. The air is so still that even the gossamer does not tremble. The reed-warblers have gone: there is no chorus of chattering and husky music to greet the new day; but presently a wren trills, a woodpecker's 'chipping' breaks the silence of the nearby woods and bull-finches utter plaintive whistles in the sallow bushes.

A pheasant wakes in a sedgy jungle roost and rises like a rocket, scattering the dew in its rude progress and raising a general alarm. The sun's warmth now begins to be felt. Soon bumble-bees are astir; wasps begin their hunting and the first dragonfly wakes with a rustle and fret of wings. The mist and its magic have evaporated: the sparkling webs have dried to near invisibility and only the recesses of the lush undergrowth are still wet. The fen is set fair for a golden day as the peacock and brimstone butterflies come swooping out to the flowers.

Ted Ellis

Broadland has been fortunate in the succession of naturalists who have studied its flora and fauna and have published their observations, providing not only a wealth of knowledge about the natural history of the region but also an insight into the changes that have occurred over the years. Norfolk as a whole has of course for long been recognized as supremely interesting for its natural history. Numerous observers have contributed, in the course of a wider coverage of the county at large, to the corpus of knowledge which has been progressively built up about the Broads. Publications have ranged from articles and notes in the *Transactions of the*

Opposite:
The Broadland Conservation Centre: the Norfolk Naturalists' Trust's floating demonstration centre on Ranworth Broad.
M. K. Ewans

Norfolk and Norwich Naturalists' Society and other journals to such magisterial publications as Henry Stevenson's *Birds of Norfolk*, published between 1866 and 1890, and B. B. Riviere's *History of the Birds of Norfolk*, published in 1930. There have also been many books, articles and notes dealing specifically with the flora and fauna of the Broads. While it would be an impossible task to provide an account of the voluminous literature which has appeared over the years, it is worth looking at some half dozen naturalists who might be regarded as particularly Broads oriented. This is not only because they are fascinating writers, but also because they have provided between them much essential evidence for the conviction that the Broads are of exceptional conservation importance.

The first of these naturalists was Sir Thomas Browne. After he had studied at Oxford and had graduated as a doctor of physic at Leyden, he took up residence in Norwich in 1637 and lived there as a respected doctor and man of letters until his death in 1682. Browne's considerable reputation derives principally from his first published work, *Religio Medici*, in which he set out his faith as a Christian and as a doctor. But he was also fortunate in living in a period when there was a strong revival of interest in natural history. His *Notes and Letters on the Natural History of Norfolk*, which dates from 1662 onwards, owes much to the habit of systematic observation which he acquired from his medical training and which was a feature of the new approach to zoology he shared with several of his contemporaries, notably Francis Willoughby and John Ray. He was, for example, convinced about migration, not accepting the widely held theory that hibernation accounted for the absence of many species of birds in the winter months, although this theory had not been wholly abandoned more than a century later when Gilbert White was writing. Browne noted that birds

> wch come in the spring coming for the most part from the southward those wch come in the Autumn or winter from the northward. so that they are observed to come in great flocks with a north east wind & to depart with a south west. nor to come only in flocks of one kind butt teals woodcocks felfars thrushes and small birds to come and light together. for the most part some hawkes & birds of pray attending them.

Though Browne makes a number of observations on fish, his main interest was clearly birds. He makes a series of fascinating remarks about particular species, revealing, for example, that the heronry at Reedham (now, alas, deserted even by herons) was at one time a nesting site for cormorants and spoonbills:

> The platea or shovelard wch build upon the topps of high trees. They

have formerly built in the Hernerie at Claxton & Reedham now at Trinley in Suffolk. they come in march & are shot by fowlers not for their meat butt the handsomenesse of the same, remarkable in their white colour copped crowne & spoone or spatule like bill . . . Cormorants. Building at Reedham upon trees from whence King charles the first was wont to be supplied.

He refers to a pelican which was shot on Horsey Fen on 22nd May, 1663, "wch stuffed & cleaned I yet retain", but was careful to note that one had recently escaped from the King's collection at St James's Park and that this might be the same bird. His notes include references to cranes, white-tailed eagles (he is careful to rule out the presence of golden eagles in Norfolk), ospreys, hen harriers, marsh harriers and bustards, which were "not infrequent in the champlain & fieldie part of this county". He describes the harriers as "the gray and bald Buzzard of all wch the great number of broad waters and warrens makes no small number". He notes that cranes were less numerous than in earlier years, although "often seen here in hard winters". He dissected many birds and collected the skins of many others (until his collection was destroyed during an outbreak of plague). He kept a bittern in his garden for two years and also tried to keep a pair of shearwaters, although he gave up after five weeks because they had to be forcibly fed with fish—they then died after seventeen days without food. He includes an unmistakable description of a roller and refers to the great skua, "one whereof was shot at Hickling while 2 thereof were feeding upon a dead horse". He describes avocets and hoopoes as "not infrequent". A vivid impression can be derived from his writings of the extent to which eggs, wildfowl and birds generally formed part of the common diet of his times. The bustard was "a dayntie dish", the dotterel "excellent" and godwits "the dayntiest": the redshank, however, was "no dayntie dish". For a wedding in 1667, there were sent "out of the marshland in Norfolk . . . nine cranes, nine swans and sixteen bitterns, with a large number of other wildfowl".

He also reports:

Sir Thomas Browne.
Norfolk Library Services

> The great number of rivers riuulets & plashes of water makes hernes & herneries to abound in these parts. young hernsies being esteemed a festiuall dish & much desired by some palates . . . Larus alba or puets [probably common gulls] in such plentie about Horsey that they sometimes bring them in carts to norwich & sell them at small rates. & the country people make use of their eggs in puddings & otherwise. great plentie thereof have bred about scoulton meere & from thence sent to London.

Browne never completed his own natural history of Norfolk, but he contributed to the efforts of those he considered better

Heron at nest. There is still a heronry at Hickling, although others have disappeared from the Broads area.
Norfolk Naturalists' Trust

naturalists than himself. He put coloured drawings and other material at the disposal of John Ray and corresponded with a friend, Dr Merrett, to assist him in compiling an encyclopaedia of natural history. But there can be no doubt about his own originality and keenness of observation, nor of his genuinely scientific outlook, which is exemplified by his concern for accurate classification (a good half-century before Linnaeus): "I confess for such little birds I am much unsatisfied on the names given to many by countrymen, and uncertantie what to giue them myself, or to what classes of authors clearly to reduce them." John Evelyn writes of him:

> Next morning I went to see Sir Thomas Browne; his whole house and garden being a paradise and cabinet of rarities, and that of the best collection, especially medals, books, plants and natural things. Amongst

46

Marsh harrier at nest.
Norfolk Naturalists' Trust

other curiosities, Sir Thomas had a collection of the eggs of all the fowl and birds he could procure, that country (especially the promontory of Norfolk) being frequented, as he said, by several kinds which seldom or never go farther into the land, as cranes, storks, eagles, and variety of water fowl.

Within Norfolk, Browne remained in a class of his own for some 150 years. In the eighteenth and early nineteenth centuries the area was an attraction for a number of people whose main interest was in wildfowling but who were also naturalists and collectors. But it was not until 1834 that the eminent Victorian surgeon, Sir James Paget, and his brother compiled their *Sketch of the Natural History of Yarmouth and its Neighbourhood*, the significance of which was that it represented the first attempt to produce a comprehensive, systematic flora and fauna of the region, with a

47

brief indication of how common each species was. One of their conclusions was that nearly all the mammalia were either totally extinct or in the process of extinction. So far as birds were concerned, their book was written very much from the point of view of the collector; among other points of interest they noted that red-headed geese and harlequin duck were for sale in Yarmouth market, that six glossy ibises had been seen on Breydon in 1924—two of which had been shot—and that several spoonbills were generally shot there each spring.

The Pagets were soon followed by the Reverend Richard Lubbock, whose *Observations on the Fauna of Norfolk, and More Particularly on the District of the Broads* was published in 1845. After graduating from Cambridge, Lubbock held a number of curacies in Norfolk and soon made a name for himself in local natural history circles, becoming a member of the Committee of Norwich Museum in 1831. In 1837, he became rector of Eccles, a parish near Attleborough in south Norfolk, where he remained for nearly forty years until his death in 1876. Apart from notes on mammals (in which he agrees with the Pagets about the growing scarcity of species), river fish and, above all, birds, the *Fauna* includes sections on the practice of falconry in Norfolk and on decoys. While admitting to being a sportsman himself, he noted the diminution in the numbers of marsh birds—"our marshes are more and more improved and drained, for the sake of patronage; and under the plea of gathering lapwings' eggs, almost all the birds which remain in summer have their nests regularly plundered". He observed that in 1821 a single egger from Potter Heigham had taken 160 dozen lapwing eggs from the adjacent marshes, and that other eggs, including those of redshank, reeve and tern, had been taken at the same time. Early in the season eggs might fetch eightpence each, but never less than three shillings a dozen. Ruffs were also diminishng, being caught by means of horsehair snares as they congregated on their "hills" in the breeding season. "Loons" (great crested grebes) were shot for the sake of their feathers—"perhaps the next generation may speak of this bird, as we do now of bustards, in the past tense" (although here he was, happily, mistaken). He also castigated landowners for their "senseless persecution" of hawks, which had contributed to an "enormous increase of vermin". Yet he himself rented shooting rights in the Broads, killed eleven bitterns in a single year in the course of wildfowling excursions, and also shot and snared ruffs. On the one hand, therefore, he undoubtedly possessed a faculty for the acute observation and fascinating description of wildlife, but at the same time, like many of his contemporaries, he was highly ambivalent on the question of conservation. He rightly deserves Henry Stevenson's two-edged compliment, "To him we owe, as an author, the

Great crested grebe. The photographer noted "This bird shouted disapproval and put on a most impressive act each time the shutter of the camera clicked."
Norfolk Naturalists' Trust

first recognition of the Broad District of Norfolk, as a paradise for the gunner and angler"; but his *Fauna* is nevertheless a classic, though rarely recognized as such.

In coming to Arthur Patterson, we meet not only a considerable character but perhaps the most distinguished and certainly the most prolific of the Broadland naturalists. Patterson was born in 1857 in one of the Yarmouth "rows", the squalid and unhealthy alleyways which ran in a gridiron pattern from the market down to the wharves. His mother died when he was three and the conditions in which he was brought up were such that he was the only one of a family of nine to survive to adulthood. His father, who was a shoemaker, insurance agent and active Primitive Methodist, inadvertently aroused a love of nature in the young Patterson by taking him to his allotment just outside Yarmouth. There the boy could observe the ditch prawns, leeches, dragonflies and other natural curiosities with which it abounded. From that moment he was hooked as a naturalist.

49

Patterson's life was for many years a struggle against poverty and adversity. The beginnings of a career as a teacher were interrupted by ill-health, and thereafter he took a succession of jobs as an insurance agent, postman, peddler of tea, warehouseman and agent for Singer sewing machines. He tried unsuccessfully to start a career as a zoo keeper, first in Preston and then in Dublin, and was compelled, again for health reasons, to turn down the offer of an appointment at London Zoo. To keep the wolf from the door and to buy natural history books, he made and sold stuffed animals including toads; and at intervals he took to the roads as a showman, on one occasion with an armadillo and on another with a stuffed Rorqual whale. It was not until he reached the age of thirty-four that he achieved some degree of security as a school attendance officer, an occupation which gave him time for his nature studies.

Patterson had a natural talent for drawing and gradually acquired a reputation as a cartoonist, blackboard artist and lecturer. He also developed skills in writing, his first letter to the press, about kingfishers, appearing when he was twenty-one. As a writer his energy and creativity were immense. He turned out over the years twenty-eight books and hundreds of articles and letters. He also kept a systematic daily record of his observations over a period of some fifty years. One of his areas of expertise was fish: he doubled the list of Yarmouth species and added thirty to the Norfolk fauna, and he contributed articles on fish to the *Zoologist* for around twenty years. His *Catalogue of the Birds of Great Yarmouth*, published in 1901, was the first to be produced since that of the Pagets. For forty years or so he contributed to the *Transactions of the Norfolk and Norwich Naturalists' Society*. As John Knowlittle, his articles for the *Eastern Daily Press* made him a by-word throughout East Anglia.

Patterson was exceptional in that he was able to establish close relationships with the race of solitary and independent punt gunners and fishermen who frequented Breydon, of whom he left a unique record in his books *Wild Life on a Norfolk Estuary* and *Wildfowlers and Poachers*. He was never happier than when roughing it in one of his succession of houseboats, hobnobbing with the Breydoners and marshmen, or cruising in his Breydon punt, the *Yarwhelp*.

Arthur Patterson's achievements were little known outside his native Norfolk. He was proposed as a member of the Linnaean Society as early as 1909 by no less a person than the notorious "Flying Duchess" of Bedford, with whom he had struck up a somewhat bizarre acquaintance, but it was not until the end of his life that he achieved even this limited recognition. He has, unlike Gilbert White, never become a cult figure, but his books and diaries give a no less fascinating picture of the wildlife of east Norfolk than White's do of Selborne.

Among other naturalists who spanned the century was M. C. Cooke, a native of Horning who became an international authority on fungi and put together a prodigious collection of some forty-six thousand specimens.

Two other Broads naturalists of a rather different stamp were Jim Vincent and Emma Turner, both of whom worked, often together, on Hickling Broad. In 1909 the shooting rights at Whiteslea Lodge at Hickling were acquired by the Hon. Edwin Montagu, later to be Secretary of State for India, and Sir Edward Grey, then Foreign Secretary. The happy outcome was that they decided to restrict their shooting to common species and to manage the estate for conservation purposes. Jim Vincent, whom they appointed as their keeper, has left as his legacy not only the Hickling nature reserve itself but also an ornithological diary for 1911. Montagu had this printed with illustrations by George Lodge, who also illustrated Bannerman's *The Birds of the British Isles*, and the outcome was a delightful book, compiled by an acute and knowledgeable observer, giving an account of the many birds which were to be found on Hickling in a single year. Emma Turner, for her part, was not only a naturalist and author but also

Jim Vincent showing his sister Ida how to operate a double-barrelled 4-bore punt gun.
Ida Grosvenor

an accomplished bird photographer. Her book *Broadland Birds* was illustrated with her own photographs and was the outcome of long periods spent camping and observing on Hickling Broad on her houseboat, which was moored at what came to be known as Emma's Island. In 1911 she and Jim Vincent recorded the first bitterns to breed in Britain since they had ceased to feature as breeding birds some forty years previously.

In 1923, when Arthur Patterson was in his sixties, he was approached by a boy by the name of Ted Ellis who was at that time barely in his teens but was already a budding naturalist in very much the same mould as himself. The two of them remained friends and collaborators up to the time of Patterson's death, and Ellis helped the older man to produce *Wildfowlers and Poachers*. From the time of his childhood in Guernsey, Ellis had, like Patterson, been intrigued by the natural world around him and he started to write his nature notebooks at the age of twelve, soon after he and his family moved to Yarmouth. He left school at fifteen, and like Patterson's, his career might have taken an altogether different turn but for illness. He also had the misfortune to miss, by sheer accident, an appointment at the BBC in London. But such was his

Arthur Patterson in his Breydon Punt.
Norfolk Library Services

reputation and the impressiveness of his nature notebooks that in 1928, when he was only nineteen, with no secondary education and no formal qualifications, he was appointed to the post of Natural History Assistant at the Castle Museum, Norwich. There, amid other duties, he composed the dioramas of Norfolk wildlife which can still be seen in what is now the Ted Ellis Norfolk Room, undertook various programmes of research and put together a comprehensive catalogue of the Norfolk flora and fauna. His career also blossomed in three other directions: he wrote regular nature articles for the *Eastern Daily Press*, the *Eastern Evening News* and subsequently *The Guardian* and later branched into radio and television, becoming a household figure throughout East Anglia and beyond; he specialized in the field of microfungi, in which he became a leading authority; and he discovered Wheatfen, where he and his family eventually went to live in 1946.

Ted Ellis.
Eastern Daily Press

Wheatfen is an area of some 130 acres situated on the south bank of the Yare a few miles downstream from Norwich, between Surlingham and Rockland Broads. It has been described as the richest, most diverse fenland habitat in East Anglia, with twice the flora of the better known Wicken Fen in Cambridgeshire. Its uniqueness lies in the fact that it is a complex of highly diverse environments—woodland, carr, reed-beds and waterways—the whole comprising a freshwater area which is also tidal. Thanks to Ted Ellis, it is particularly valuable in that it has been studied comprehensively over a period of half a century, with the result that much is known about the changes and successions that have taken place. The whole area is now a Grade I Site of Special Scientific Interest (SSSI).

As a writer, when he was not contributing to the *Transactions of the British Mycological Society*, Ted Ellis's forte was the newspaper article, where he had the knack of presenting often complicated accounts of natural processes in terms that would both enlighten and fascinate the reader. His *magnum opus* was the book *The Broads*, published in 1965, which remains the definitive work on the natural history of the area. He wrote six of its fifteen chapters himself, on flowering plants, cryptogamic plants, insects, fishes, amphibians and reptiles, and mammals. He also wrote the chapter on birds in collaboration with B. B. Riviere, whose reputation is secure as the foremost Norfolk ornithologist of this century. Prominent among the other naturalists who contributed was Robert Gurney, an expert on Broads water zoology who, with his brother Eustace, founded the pioneer freshwater laboratory at Sutton Broad in 1906. Geology and human activity were also covered. Dr Joyce Lambert wrote on the vegetation of Broadland and, with colleagues, on the origin of the Broads, while Ellis himself rounded off the book with appendices listing the Broads' insects and Broadland marsh tools.

These were just a few of the naturalists who have helped to put together a record of the natural life of the Broads; and there have been many others, some of them also of appreciable eminence, who have contributed in no less measure. Ted Ellis was perhaps the last in the great tradition of Broadland field naturalists who between them established the scientific and taxonomic basis on which all current knowledge and studies are founded. Subsequently, progress has taken place broadly in two directions. First, the type of survey of species which was started by the Pagets and continued by Patterson, Ellis and others has been developed on a collaborative and even more thorough and comprehensive basis. Within the last few years, for example, the Norfolk and Norwich Naturalists' Society has, with the help of a large team of observers, produced as full a record as possible of the breeding birds of Norfolk. This suggests that Broadland may currently possess some 120 breeding species. In conjunction with the Norfolk Ornithologists' Association and a small army of contributors, the society also publishes an annual *Norfolk Bird and Mammal Report*. The other path of development essentially follows that pioneered by Ellis in his comprehensive, ongoing study of the ecology of Wheatfen. Later examples of this type of integrated study of Broadland environments would doubtless be regarded as more scientific and professional, although this would not be to decry the achievements of any of the men and women who have been described here. Although some of them were amateurs or at least lacking in formal scientific training, they were the first to survey in detail the astoundingly rich wetland of the Broads. Along this second route, the Department of Environment Studies of the University of East Anglia have carried out programmes of research that have been vital in analysing the deterioration of the Broadland natural environment in recent years and in suggesting courses of action which might ameliorate matters. Some of their achievements are described in the second part of this book.

★   ★   ★

Right: *Bearded tit.*
RSPB

Below: *Short-eared owl.*
RSPB

Broads cruising in traditional style.
P. A. Ewans

Barton Staithe.
Martin Trelawney

The Broads as Local Playground   5

The Broad is all animation, and the shore has pleasant scenes . . .
The broad grassy staithe is thronged by people who have come on
foot or on wheels, thickest about the booth where cakes and ale are
to be had, and a dance by and by . . . The Committee's barge, an
imposing looking vessel, crowded with company, and the band of the
Norfolk Volunteer Artillery, anchored near the starting buoy,
attracts every ear by its sonorous music, and presently by the report
of a cannon, which rumbles through the woods, and soon after this
signal three cutters start to sail round the course . . . Some of the
yachts display flags enough for a whole fleet, and their decks are
thronged with spectators, among whom appear the comely faces of
English maidens, and the wherries, with their double rows of seats
closely packed, exhibit company of all degrees . . . Here and there
one strikes up music on its own account; another, provided with an
temporary bar, is emptying its beer barrels, and all exhibit signs of
active eating and drinking . . . Except a few yachtsmen and
wherrymen, there seems to be no one who takes an interest in the
sailing match . . . if constant eating and drinking may be taken as
evidence, dinner-time lasts all day.

Walter White at Wroxham Regatta, 1865

In Norwich Castle Museum hangs Joseph Stannard's magnificent
picture *Thorpe Water Frolic, 1824.* The scene portrayed is of a
medley of boats, their brown and white sails and coloured pennants
drooping lazily in a light air, against the background of the wooded
shore of the river and of Thorpe Old Hall on the hill behind. In the
foreground, on his yacht *Sylph,* is the owner of the hall, Colonel
John Harvey, resplendent in navy tail coat and grey top hat.
Around him are ladies in pastel dresses and bonnets, a uniformed
band is playing, and a variety of punts and skiffs are shuttling
passengers between ships and shore. Seamen in shirt sleeves and
knitted caps lean over the rails of their craft, flagons and tankards
are in evidence, a small boy trails a model boat, and Stannard
himself—a keen yachtsman—surveys the scene in a red coat from a
smart white yacht with a green and gilded stern. Racing is perhaps
over for the day, for the picture suggests that drinking and dining
rather than competition are the priorities of the moment.

"Thorpe Water Frolic, 1824": Joseph Stannard's painting, now in the Norwich Castle Museum.
Norfolk Museums Service

Such water frolics were a traditional feature of the Broadland scene and regular events on many of the rivers and broads. The oldest one was possibly the Burgh Water Frolic, first mentioned in 1577 and held at the western end of Breydon Water. It was customary for the Mayor and Corporation of Yarmouth to sail to the frolic in state, in a specially fitted-out wherry, accompanied by another with a band. Once the racing had ended, the company went ashore for lunch and later watched aquatic sports and fireworks. The Thorpe Frolic was started by Colonel Harvey on his return from Venice in 1821 and was said to have been attended by twenty thousand people, two fifths of the population of Norwich. An account has survived of a cruise on the Broads in September, 1818, by a party of yachtsmen who sailed what they described as a "pleasure boat", the *Britannia*, from Norwich to Wroxham, where they participated in a three-day frolic with a dozen or so other yachts. On the first day, starting from anchor—as seems to have been usual in those days—the course was twice round a number of stakes set in the broad, while the second and third days were occupied with races to and from Horning. The *Britannia* did not distinguish herself (owing, it was alleged, to light winds) and went aground in the river. She also appeared to have let in the rain;

there is more than one reference to soaking bedding. By today's standards, her rigging seems to have been excessively complicated, with a topmast and crosstrees, and "a bowline to the topsail and a ringtail", which appears to have been an extra sail rigged abaft the boom. But there is no doubting the enthusiasm of the crew and the keenness of the racing. In the same year there was a frolic at Beccles that included a race for eight boats, again including the *Britannia*. A "private match for £5" and rowing races followed, and finally there was a display of fireworks and a ball in the Ship's Tavern, North Quay. The dress for these occasions seems to have been fairly formal; Start's print of the Mutford Water Frolic of 1827 depicts sailors in tails, white trousers and large curly-brimmed toppers.

About this time the "lateener" was introduced to the Broads, reportedly by an army officer who had been stationed in Malta and had become enthusiastic about this typical Mediterranean rig. By 1850 there were said to be a large number of them competing in local regattas. The lateener was to all appearances a dangerously over-canvased craft. Its main feature was an enormous triangular sail set on a boom and yard and hoisted on a mast in the bows, aft of which was a mizzen mast with another lateen sail or gaff mizzen (sometimes with a mizzen topsail) that was not much smaller. Its advantage on the narrow Broads rivers was that it could sail very close to the wind. One of the early lateeners, the *Vampire*, was a ten-tonner with a fore-yard sixty-three feet long, but the most famous was the *Maria*, built in 1827 and sailed for many years by Sir Jacob Preston of Beeston Hall. The *Maria* and Colonel Harvey's *Sylph* were great rivals, but so fast was the *Maria* that at one regatta at Wroxham no other craft was prepared to sail against her. Sir Jacob died in 1894, but the *Maria* (known to some as the "old black *Maria*") was still being sailed up to the outbreak of the First World War. Her hull was for many years in a boatshed on Barton Broad, but it has since been rescued and is now in the Yarmouth Maritime Museum. Oliver Ready's description of one of the *Maria*'s competitors, the *Thorn*, gives some idea of the lateener's rig and sailing qualities:

> Her actual hull was about fourteen feet long, though an enormous square eight-foot counter stern lying almost clear of the water, gave her a length overall of, say, twenty-two feet. Half-decked, bows broad and bluff, and a nine-foot beam, she presented a very tubby appearance, though below water her lines were fine, with a two-foot iron keel and a large rudder swinging below the counter. . . . Her short, thick foremast, stepped right in the bows with a strong rake forrard, carried an enormous lateen sail with a yard about forty feet long, and an eighteen-foot boom swinging just clear of the mizzen-mast. Almost burying herself in the water, throwing up a big bow-wave, and drawing a small

mountain astern, her enormous sail-spread still forced her along at great speed, and she would roar majestically by with all the power and swell of a steam launch. Beating close to the wind was her strong point, for besides sailing very close, she went about like a flash, and without losing hardly any way; while running before a strong breeze was dangerous work, as her towering mainsail, pressing down on the foremast raking right over the bows, forced her further and further into the water, till she would crash along, bows level, with all hands congregated on the counter to keep her from running under.

Racing was more usually between cruising yachts with a straightforward sloop rig, although even they had some peculiarities. The hull's centre of lateral resistance tended to be rather forward, which meant that a large rudder was required, while the jib was set on a bowsprit which might project as much as twenty-six feet in front of the bows. Even so, going about tended to be a problem, and the bowsprit was all too likely to get caught in the reeds. Their gaff mainsails were supplemented for racing by large square-headed topsails, and ballast was provided by as many crew as could be packed on board. Races between trading wherries also began to be included in the regatta programmes and attracted keen competition. On one occasion two wherries fouled, the crews started fighting and when the boats separated they had the wrong crews. These crews nevertheless sailed the remainder of the race with undiminished enthusiasm. One of the most successful trading wherries was *Fawn*, built in 1875 and owned by one Isaac Wales, a timber merchant of Reedham. It apparently won at Lowestoft regatta for six years running. The skipper, Ophir Powley, is said to have carried a pair of racing pigeons on board which he would release after passing the finishing line to inform the owner of the success.

As the years went by, the old, festive water frolics became well-managed regattas and everything became more formalized. In the eighteen-eighties, for example, Wroxham regatta was inaugurated at 8 am on the first day by the firing of a gun, at which point all the assembled yachts were "dressed overall" with flags and bunting. Racing was regulated from a trading wherry anchored in the broad, while another contained a band. Races were held for cruisers, open and half-decked boats, wherries, hired cruisers and watermen, and sometimes for four-oared rowing boats and motor boats. An entry in a diary for 1880 reads: "22nd July. Wroxham Regatta, apparently first public regatta. Band £20. Fireworks in evening. Bishop Hartley dropped sirloin of beef overboard, hung up to dry, none the worse".

The first yacht club to be formed on the Broads was apparently the Amateur Yacht Club, set up in 1855. It survived for only three months, the founding members having spent all its funds on the inaugural cruise. A more serious venture was

launched in 1859 when a number of "boating gentlemen" met together and founded the Norfolk and Suffolk Yacht Club. This initiative resulted partly from the increasing popularity of yacht racing and partly from a growing inability to control the behaviour of the professional watermen who crewed the yachts. The previous year the crews of two racing yachts had boarded one another, lashed their craft together and fought out their differences to the bitter end. The club held regattas around the Broads and also organized cruises in company. Three racing classes were recognized—Cutter, Lateen, and Lateen Foresail and Mizzen. Handicapping was on a tonnage basis, a modification of the Thames Measurement being used. Professional watermen were normally employed to do the actual sailing; it was not until 1876 that a cup was presented for yachts crewed by "gentlemen amateurs" only. The cruises tended to be highly formal; from among the

A lateener, probably the Ariel, on the Waveney. Norfolk Museums Service

59

participants a commodore was appointed on whose yacht the company would gather for the evening's conviviality. One such cruise in 1884 included fourteen yachts and two wherries, one the "messroom" and the other the "Ladies' Hotel". On the first day the fleet sailed to Beccles, where they had "fireworks and lanterns and a concert and tales on the wherry until 12.30 am". On the next day, a Sunday, the company went in dinghies to church and later had "dinner and hymns" on the wherry. They then sailed to Oulton Broad, where they "all laid up together and dined on wherry and sing song until late". Having taken part in the local regatta, they finally sailed to Reedham.

Emphasizing the trend towards amateur sailing, a second club, the Yare Sailing Club, was formed in 1879 to cater for amateurs only. This club was at first based at Thorpe and held regattas at various points as far downstream as Cantley. By the turn of the century it was holding regattas at a number of places between Horning and Beccles. Later, having been renamed the Yare and Bure Yacht Club, it was said to be the largest sailing club in the world, with a membership of nearly six hundred. A separate trend was a certain disillusionment with handicapped racing, which encouraged the expensive business of building new boats designed mainly to circumvent some restriction in the handicapping rules. At the turn of the century the Norfolk and Suffolk Yacht Club, by that time "Royal", commissioned the designer Linton Hope to produce a fleet of identical yachts that could compete on equal terms. The outcome was the half-decked Broads One-design, more commonly known as the "Brown Boat", the main feature of which was a slender brown-varnished hull with a shallow spoon-shaped bow. A few years later, the Yare and Bure Yacht Club followed suit with the Yare and Bure One-design, designed by Ernest Woods and more commonly known as the "White Boat". This design had a somewhat shorter hull, but with a bowsprit. By the Second World War, thirty Brown Boats and fifty-eight White Boats had been built, and they had been joined in 1928 by the very similar Yarmouth One-design and Waveney One-design.

The Broads was also one of the birthplaces of dinghy racing. This became increasingly popular in the eighteen-eighties and was formally recognized by the Yare Sailing Club in 1887. In 1894 the Broads Dinghy Club was formed. Rules for a restricted class of fourteen-foot lugsail dinghies were drawn up in the eighteen-nineties and a fleet of these continued to be sailed over the next half century. Together with the West of England Conference Dinghy, this Norfolk Dinghy was the direct ancestor of the International Fourteen-foot Dinghy.

Between the two world wars, yacht racing on the Broads became both keener and more diversified. The International

White Boats: Yare and Bure One-designs racing on Wroxham Broad.
J. R. Marr

Norfolk One-design Dinghies. Designed by Herbert Woods in 1930, these dinghies are still being raced on the Broads.
Eastern Daily Press

Fourteen-foot was adopted, and those who raced them included the well-known dinghy sailors Peter Scott, John Winter and Stewart Morris. As the Internationals became more sophisticated and expensive, a demand grew for a one-design dinghy that was affordable to sailors of limited means. The result was the Norfolk One-design, designed by Herbert Woods and at first sponsored by the Broads Sailing and Motor Club, which was experiencing unacceptable limitations on speedboat racing by the crowded state of the rivers and the imposition of speed limits. Six boats sailed in the first race of the class, from Potter Heigham to Hickling and back, on Easter Monday, 1931. By 1933 the class numbered twenty boats, and thirty-nine had been built by 1939.

Perhaps the most intriguing of the inter-war racing boats were the Norfolk Punts. These were a direct adaptation of the Hickling gun punt, with a shallow draft and very similar lines, and the specification required that they should be "suited to the purpose of being quanted, rowed or sailed to fowl". They carried a large spread of sail for their length of between twenty and twenty-two feet, and they were exceedingly fast and could plane in a hard wind up to a speed of some sixteen knots. They required a highly acrobatic helmsman and crew. Within a year or two of their adoption as a class, the Norfolk Punt Club's regatta at Wroxham had a dozen or more punts competing in three races, one of them for lady helmswomen, with additional races for One-designs and fourteen-foot dinghies. At the Hickling regatta of 1930 there were three races for boats of any rig. These were dominated by the Great Yarmouth One-designs but punts were in close contention. Other races were for punts alone and for fourteen-foot dinghies, the latter being won by a considerable distance by Stewart Morris. The day finished with quanting and rowing races and "aquatic sports". The wherry *Zulu* was used as the committee boat. In spirit, as well as in standards of organization and diversity of the types of boats sailing, there was by then a good deal of difference from the traditional "water frolics". Foul sailing was a thing of the past and any controversy was sorted out by a system of formal "protests" rather than by rows and fights at the end of the racing. As one observer put it, "There was no such thing as a protest in my young days. The crews landed on the bank and fought it out with their fists if there was any disagreement."

The Broads thus developed over a period of rather more than a century as an arena in which local residents could race and cruise in a variety of craft, many of them specifically developed for the requirements of the local waters. The yacht clubs themselves also developed and changed, the Yare and Bure, spurred on by the opportunity to acquire the lease of Wroxham Broad, finally amalgamating in 1937 with the Great Yarmouth Yacht Club, the

WROXHAM BROAD

Wroxham Regatta, 1928: Norfolk Punts, One-designs and 14ft National (later International) Dinghies feature prominently.

THURSDAY, JULY 19th,

Norfolk Punt Club Regatta.

Start 10-30 a.m.

Sailed under the Rules of the Norfotk and Suffolk Regatta Association.

Race 1. **NORFOLK BROADS & YARE AND BURE O.D.C.** Sweepstakes
Entry Fee 5/-

Race 2. **NORFOLK GUN PUNTS. Classes A and B.**

Rule 3. **14 ft. NATIONAL DINGHIES. Sweepstakes.**
Entry Fee 5/-

Race 4. **NORFOLK GUN PUNTS, Classes A and B.** (Invitation Race.)

Race 5. **HALF-DECKED RESTRICTED CLASS & Gt. YARMOUTH ONE DESIGN CLASS SAILS. Sweepstakes.** Entry Fee 5/-

Rule 6. **NORFOLK GUN PUNTS, Classes A and B.** (Ladies to steer.)

C. R. HOWLETT, Hon. Sec.

Bunting, Printer, St. Miles, Norwich.

Horning Town Sailing Club and the Norfolk Dinghy Club to form the Norfolk Broads Yacht Club. But there were, of course, other pursuits occupying the leisure time of the Broadland inhabitants. Coursing was a favourite sport, and people are said to have come from as far as Newmarket to participate on the Ludham Marshes. Coot shoots were also popular, the objective being to pick a moment when there was an influx of birds from the Continent, assemble as many boats and guns as possible, and mount an organized "drive" across an open sheet of water. At a shoot on Hickling Broad in February, 1934, over twelve hundred coots were slaughtered in this way. Wildfowling generally was highly popular and shooting rights were regularly hired by *aficionados.* The sportsman's and wildfowler's "Bible" was Nicholas Everitt's *Broadland Sport*, published in 1902. This covered everything—an account of a cruise in the wherry *Warrior*; descriptions of places; anecdotes

A coot shoot on the Broads. An illustration to a magazine article of 1918.

galore; advice on shooting of every description; the use of decoys; punt gunning; fishing for tench, pike and eels; otter hunting and even the use of stalking horses to approach wildfowl. To this was added an account of the development of yacht racing and the Broads yacht clubs.

Some idea of the lifestyle to be enjoyed on the Broads is provided by the diaries of the Reverend Edward Wymer, who was the vicar of Ingham from 1827 to 1873. Mr Wymer owned a succession of boats and habitually sailed from early spring through to late autumn. In 1836 he was rigging his boat in February and March and was still sailing her in December. In 1844 there was five days' racing on Hickling, and in 1850 he joined a "Water Party" at Norwich which "consisted of thirty-nine men, women and children, and a good jollification it was. Did not get off the water till 9.30." Regattas and frolics were, from his account, frequent and widespread. In 1855 he was sailing a lateener to Yarmouth regatta and thence to Lowestoft, where he raced with "seven schooners and about twenty others of various sizes". He left after racing at mid-day, made Yarmouth for lunch at 3.30 and was at Acle by 8 pm. He started out the following day at about 10 am, reached Barton by 3 pm, laid up the craft and walked home. At the end of October, he was still sailing, but somewhat less comfortably:

> At Ludham Bridge a gale sprang up and we could carry on no further than just past Grapes' [a reference to the Chequers Inn at St Benet's which, together with the St Benet's windpump, was at that time run by the Grapes family]. A precious night it was. The gale continued and it rained in torrents. We were lucky in having a wherry close by us, where we got into the cabin and cooked our potatoes and partridges and dried our clothes. Moored next night at Yarmouth, the weather still being very coarse. We dined, and then went to the inn to tea and sleep. The following day over Breydon the wind and rain came on most bitterly. Finally at Reedham we handed over the boat to the bridge-keeper. Here ended our voyage of nothing but wind, snow, hail and rain. Enough to sicken a cat!

On various occasions he was in collision with a wherry and lost a bowsprit, stove in his washboard against St Olaves' bridge, was carried against Yarmouth bridge, twice blew away his foresail on a run from Acle to Breydon, ran aground at Berney Arms and carried away his foremast, and capsized on Barton with the vicar of Irstead. On one passage from Oulton he carried away the rudder hooks, shroud lanyards, quant and finally jib.

Nor were sailing and racing by any means the only pastimes which the vicar pursued. His diaries portray also a variety of other pleasures and pursuits, as well as giving a vivid account of the more serious aspects of the local life of those times. He was keenly interested in fishing (among other things for trout, which were apparently not rare in those days), shooting and coursing. He followed the hounds; attended a shoot at Ingham at which 226 birds were killed; shot blackbirds, rooks and larks; and liggered for pike, catching more than forty on one day and thirty-six on another. He skated on the Broads when they were frozen; sketched and painted; played quoits, bowls and cricket; and organized archery competitions. He attended balls, concerts, races and steeplechases. He painted his boats, thatched his boathouse, built his own chicken sheds, threshed his corn, carried his hay, fattened his pigs and took them to market, gathered his apples and planted trees. He did not, apparently, neglect his professional duties, whether in his parish or beyond: at one time he was chaplain to the High Sheriff of Norwich and preached in the cathedral. His diaries also portrayed the vicissitudes of the times: cattle plague and cholera are recorded, as well as gales which appear to have been no less serious than those experienced in the late twentieth century. In 1860, for example, he records three thousand trees as having been blown down in Westwick, as well as numerous stacks and houses.

Yarmouth anchorage. Pleasure yachts at Yarmouth around the turn of the century.

Natural calamities are, however, comparatively rare; and for Broadsmen who possessed both leisure and means, life could be both full and varied, with an ease and privilege which were denied to the majority of their fellows.

The Broads as National Playground 6

Since the first appearance of this Handbook, the Broad District has become highly popular. Each year the tourist stream increases, but, happily, there is still plenty of room. No doubt some of the old habitués, who liked to have the whole landscape to themselves, grumble at the change, but the less selfish persons, who happily constitute the majority, do not object to seeing a dozen yachts where formerly they saw but one, or a score of anglers where in past years but half-a-dozen might be seen . . . Artists have found out the charm of the quiet scenery of the Broads, and visit us in great numbers . . . Then littérateurs without numbers have written magazine and newspaper articles, and others, after a few days' scamper, have written exhaustive guide-books; and so the ball, which the present writer set rolling in earnest some years ago, is helped merrily forward, and the Rivers and Broads of Norfolk and Suffolk are fast becoming one of the most popular of English playgrounds.

George Christopher Davies

A number of years were to pass before the pleasures of sailing and racing on the rivers and broads ceased to be the monopoly of those who lived in or near Broadland and the region began to be "discovered" by those living further afield. There were two main reasons for the gradual growth in popularity of Broads holidays during the latter part of the Victorian era. The first was the development of opportunities for leisure and holidays together with the concept of the countryside as a place in which to enjoy them; the second was the invention of the railway, which brought this relatively remote area into easy reach of the country's main urban centres. For many of the newly affluent middle-class beneficiaries of the Industrial Revolution, the ideal place for a Norfolk holiday was one of the seaside resorts such as Cromer or Yarmouth; and the latter, already a fashionable resort late in the eighteenth century, developed extensively as a holiday centre in the latter half of the nineteenth. But there was another type of holiday-maker, more adventurous and prepared to "rough it", more attached to nature and the idea of "getting away from it all", and perhaps also more attracted to the concept of a companionable, relatively cheap, self-catering holiday. Specific interests such as painting, wildfowling, angling or natural history sometimes also influenced the choice. Angling seems to have become a particular attraction from an early stage and in 1883, evidently as part of a promotional campaign, a party from the Executive Committee of the Fisheries' Exhibition arrived at Wroxham on a special train to be entertained on a guided tour as far as St Benet's. For visitors to the Broads, the railway companies offered access and inducements in the form of tourist and excursion tickets, and from small beginnings the business of letting out boats gradually expanded across Broadland.

A further influence was the beginnings of a literature about the Broads, which often took the form of an account, or "log", of a cruise. The first of these appeared in 1865 in the shape of three chapters of a book entitled *Eastern England from the Thames to the Humber*. The author was Walter White, an experienced writer of travel books, and his picture of the Broads well repays reading for its perceptiveness and narrative skill. Subsequently, however, these logs tended to be somewhat less appealing since not only, inevitably, did they give all too similar accounts of the week or fortnight spent on the Broads, but the style adopted often strikes a later reader as excessively arch and "joky". The authors were also prone never to use a simple word or phrase when a more pretentious one was available. The first to appear, the *Log of "The Stranger"* by C. A. Campling, published in 1871, was typical of this genre: the reader soon tires of the forced humour and the frequent doggerel, and of having to translate into plain English such phrases as "piscatorial paraphernalia" (fishing gear) and "shed a tear of bitter amber" (drink a glass of beer). Another was E. M. Harvey's *The Cruise of the "Kate"*, the style of which can be judged from its subtitle, *A narrative of a very merry wherry expedition through the rivers and Broads of Norfolk and Suffolk*. Had many of these logs not preceded *Three Men in a Boat*, one would have thought that they were trying—and failing by a mile—to emulate it. As it is, however, they succeed merely in emphasizing what a *tour de force* Jerome K. Jerome's superbly humorous book is.

The doyen of the early writers about the Broads was undoubtedly George Christopher Davies, a Shropshire man by birth who came to Norwich in 1870 to serve part of his articles as a solicitor. Before long he moved to Newcastle upon Tyne, returning to Norwich in 1889 when he was forty years old. In due course he became Clerk to the County Council. From his earliest days in Norfolk Davies developed a passion for the Broads as well as for sailing, fishing, wildfowling and natural history, and it was not long before he started to write. His first publication about the Broads was *The Swan and her Crew*, a somewhat curious "book for boys".

George Christopher Davies, "the man who discovered the Broads".

The heroes of the story go sailing, have adventures and win races in the best *Boys' Own Paper* fashion, and a mild romantic interest is thrown in for good measure. The adventures mostly take place on a boat which the boys construct themselves, a highly unconvincing catamaran yawl which would, if it had sailed at all, undoubtedly have broken up at the first hint of heavy weather. The adventures, moreover, tend too often to be at the expense of the "lower orders", who are portrayed in what seems today to be a distastefully patronizing manner (although it probably raised no eyebrows at the time). The class assumptions of the period in fact show through in a distinctly unappealing way. Where the novel scores, however, is in its numerous passages on natural history, and it was no doubt these that caused Arthur Patterson to describe the book as one of the major influences to which he had been exposed during his early years. They may also have accounted for the fact that the book was a considerable success and ran into a number of editions, the last appearing in 1931. One cannot, however, help contrasting it with Oliver Ready's quite delightful *Life and Sport on the Norfolk Broads*, an autobiographical account of a young boy's experiences on the Broads in the middle years of the last century.

Davies followed up *The Swan* with two rather more serious books about the Broads, *Norfolk Broads and Rivers* and *The Handbook to the Rivers and Broads of Norfolk and Suffolk*. The latter, which appeared in 1882, is probably the most successful book ever to have been written about Broadland. By 1887 it had appeared, in a revised and enlarged format, in its tenth edition, and it eventually ran to over fifty. The first edition began with an introduction to the Broads and an account of a cruise. Later editions opened with six pages of "hitherto unwritten rules of etiquette", among other things discouraging "songs and revelry after eleven pm and bathing after eight am—ladies are not expected to turn out before eight, but after that time they are entitled to be free of any annoyance". Among the more sensible pieces of advice was the admonition, "Remember that sound travels a long way on the water, and do not criticise the people you may encounter with too loud a voice." *The Handbook* finished with some tips on fishing and yachting, the whole illustrated with a variety of lithographs. *Norfolk Broads and Rivers* was a more descriptive work, based in part on articles which Davies had already published in *Blackwood's Magazine* and elsewhere. The centrepiece of the book was an account of a cruise on his yacht, the *Coya*, but there was also a wealth of topographical material as well as descriptions of local characters and crafts, together with information about wherries, decoys, birds and fish, otters, eels, swans, floods and storms, and a host of other topics. It was not for nothing that Davies became known, not always approvingly, as "the man who found the Broads".

Another popularizer of the Broads was Ernest R. Suffling, who also wrote a pair of books. One was descriptive, *The Land of the Broads*, published in 1885, and the other practical, *How to Organise a Cruise on the Broads*, published in 1891. The first, which was aimed at "all who take an interest in one of the Quaintest and most Old-World parts of England", was not a patch on Davies' equivalent, even though it apparently sold some twenty thousand copies in its first ten years. The second was severely utilitarian, the reader being assured by Suffling at the outset that it was not just another "guide" to the Broads. He wrote that, as one with some twenty-five years' experience who had, moreover, read all the guides, he saw it as a means of making good their deficiencies and adding "many fancies of his own". Instructions on victualling featured prominently ("bacon, as a rule, is not good in Norfolk . . . draught ale very

Opposite: *Broadland windpump.*
Martin Trelawney

drinkable . . . but the spirits are of the 'condensed vitriol' order . . . some of the whisky is warranted to kill at any distance") and advice was tendered on what to bring (including "smoking apparatus" and a "tennis set for the party"). Then followed a chapter on "Dodges and Devices" ("In cold weather, if the boots are removed for comfort, the feet may be thrust into the sleeves of a coat, the body of which is then rolled round the legs and feet, serving to keep the person thoroughly warm"). Yacht cookery was also tackled ("Owing to the confined lockers on a boat, the butter and lard is apt to turn; when this happens it may be freshened by dissolving it in hot water with some salt added"). After those, chapters on accidents, routes to be sailed and "weather wisdom" are almost anticlimactic. Cabin amusements on a wet day were (no doubt wisely) included—("The young ladies will, of course, have the latest novel with them, or better still, their fancy needlework, and thus for a time they are happy, contented and busy"). But not for long, apparently, since recommendations followed thick and fast—a piano can be hired on a larger yacht for fifteen shillings a day; a banjo is often (but not always) a good idea; and, if all else fails, there is always cock-fighting—a "noisy, laughter-provoking game". When the rain stops, "by setting up a mark in a safe place, archery may be indulged in". In a rather more practical vein, the book ended with notes on fishing, shooting, sailing and skating, followed by a final section of "odds and ends". These included tips on keeping fishing boots in good condition ("fill them with barley grains or oats, and the corn will swell by reason of the moisture and keep the leather from crinkling up in drying") and the avoidance of poisonous mushrooms ("sprinkle a little salt on the under part or gills. If it turns yellow, they are poisonous, if black they may be safely eaten. Allow ten minutes for the salt to act properly").

The last twenty years of the nineteenth century saw an outpouring of these and other books on the Broads, some of which, as we have seen, stayed in print for nearly half a century. Of those which followed, the most attractive is undoubtedly W. A. Dutt's comprehensive book, *The Norfolk Broads*, which not only covered the history and contemporary life of Broadland but also described the region by season and locality. Dutt was a journalist by profession and was at one time a lobby correspondent in the House of Commons. He started to write only when ill-health caused him to return to his native Bungay. Arthur Patterson contributed a chapter on wildlife on Breydon, while the illustrations included a number of attractive water-colours by Frank Southgate.

The years between 1880 and 1890 were also remarkable for a sudden output of photographic publications on the Broads. Three men were principally involved, George Christopher Davies, J.

Left: *Aerial picture of Burgh Common.* Ivan West

71

Payne Jennings and, the most talented of the three, P. H. Emerson. Although they were all active on the Broads at around the same time, it seems, oddly enough, that they knew each other hardly, if at all. Davies' photographs at first illustrated his *Norfolk Broads and Rivers*, but in 1885 a portfolio of twenty-four was published by Jarrolds, quickly followed by a second. Very little is known about Payne Jennings other than that he lived and had a studio in Ashtead, Surrey, where he became a member of the parish council and described himself as an "Art Publisher". Somehow or other he obtained a commission from the Great Eastern Railway to photograph the Broads as part of a promotional campaign, and his pictures were to be seen for many years in that company's railway carriages. He apparently never wrote a single word for publication. The first edition of his volume of one hundred photographs, *Sun Pictures of the Norfolk Broads*, published in 1891, contains not even a preface (although an advertisement for the GER appears at the end). The second edition was given captions by E. R. Suffling.

The photographs produced by Davies and Jennings are attractive enough, and give a good impression of the scenery of Broadland and of the leisure activities connected with it, particularly of a waterborne nature. But they are essentially what might be called "picture postcard" productions, with little sense either of involvement in the life of the region or of originality of artistic composition. These deficiencies were amply compensated for by P. H. Emerson, who is in an altogether different category. Emerson was born in Cuba, where his American father was a wealthy sugar planter. In 1868, after his father had died and the Cuban War of Independence against Spain had broken out, his mother brought the family to England, where Emerson went to school at Cranleigh. All his life Emerson was an "achiever". He had a natural talent for sport and was described at Cambridge as an outstanding medical student. But by the time he had completed his MB degree he had become enthused by photography and, being fortunate enough to have independent means, adopted it as a full-time hobby, becoming absorbed by its scientific aspects as well as by its artistic ones. Typically, he soon came to dominate the photographic scene, lecturing and arguing with his contemporaries and publishing his views in a manifesto entitled *Naturalistic Photography*. Equally characteristically, having produced several volumes of quite remarkable photography within a space of a few years, he abruptly renounced it as an art form and turned to other interests, including, eventually, billiards and the writing of detective novels.

To appreciate Emerson's achievement, however, there is no need to examine the man or his theorizing—it is sufficient simply to look at his portfolios. Essentially they portray, with great sensitivity

A Winter's Morning. One of P. H. Emerson's most evocative photographs.

and insight, two things, the beauty of the Broads landscape and the nature and way of life of its inhabitants. To achieve these results, Emerson immersed himself in the area. In 1890 and 1891 he spent a whole year sailing the Broads in his converted wherry, *Maid of the Mist,* and his resulting portrayals of the landscape—above all the sixteen impressionistic and wholly beautiful photographs which appeared in his final volume, *Marsh Leaves*—are exceptional. Particularly atmospheric are his photographs of the Broads in winter. He also devoted a great deal of time to trying to get on close terms with the inhabitants, to the extent that he was even able to participate in their nocturnal poaching expeditions. Typically, he then went on record as criticizing the contemporary system of justice, under which severe fincs or jail sentences were imposed on convicted poachers by juries and benches composed of the very landowners over whose land the poaching had taken place. For his expression of these views he was branded, unfairly, as a socialist. The outcome of his involvement in the area was several portfolios that contain a remarkable pictorial record of the marshmen and their occupations, with texts over which he also took great pains. It is particularly refreshing to contrast his concern with the conditions of rural life at the time with the lack of understanding shown by Davies, Suffling and others. While Emerson saw the marshman as "wiry in body, pleasant in manner and intelligent in mind", Suffling went so far as to refer to the "natives" almost as if they were another race, and warned his readers of their "quaintness, both in language and ideas, and also in manners".

Possibly encouraged by one or other of the plethora of publications and preparing to undertake a Broads sailing holiday, the intending visitor might well have turned to the advertisements that appeared at the back of many of them. By the time that the seventh edition of Suffling's *The Land of the Broads* appeared in 1895, it contained more than fifty advertisements of yachts and boats for hire, many of them converted wherries. If Nicholas Everitt is to be believed, the first wherry to be fitted out for pleasure cruising was built in Beccles in about 1840, but it seems that wherry conversions did not become at all common until the eighteen-eighties. The pioneers appear to have been Press Brothers of North Walsham, who by 1888 were advertising five converted wherries for hire. The method of conversion was fairly simple, entailing replacing the upper parts of the hatch coamings with sides, complete with windows, and partitioning the hold into several cabins, which were then furnished. At the end of the season the hold was stripped out and the wherry reverted to trading use. A certain Mr Squirrel, for example, used his wherry, the *Sylvia*, for his business as a corn merchant in the winter and fitted her out for hiring in the summer. Later, wherries were converted permanently for pleasure hiring and a number were built specifically for the purpose. An advertisement in Suffling's book for the wherry yacht *Zoe* specifies that she was "not used at any period of the year for trading purposes". She was "panelled throughout with polished English oak" and was fully fitted, with brass bedsteads for the ladies' cabin and electric bells to summon the attendants and a "first-class pianoforte", not to omit that absolute requirement for middle-class Victorians, a water closet. The *Rambler*, built in 1898, sported a bathroom; while the *Warrior* had a photographic darkroom and "warming apparatus". Others were "magnificently fitted with every conceivable convenience, luxury and bric-a-brac, which would rival many of the best house-boats on the Thames". Some were fitted with counter sterns, so that members of the party could sit and watch the wherry being manoeuvred.

At the other end of the scale, descending through "barge yachts" and "cutter yachts" with cabins, were open centreboard boats with the sleeping accommodation arranged in the well, under an awning rigged over the boom. The cost of hiring a wherry, complete with two attendants, ranged from £8 to £20 a week.

Listing the types of craft available, Suffling describes a seventeen-ton yacht which "taken altogether, may be looked on as a cosy home by the party in occupation" and a twenty-foot boat ("In warm weather, fitted with an awning for sleeping under, it forms a snug berth for two or three persons"), the costs of hiring ranging from about £9 9s a week for the seventeen-tonner to about £2 10s for the twenty-footer. A catalogue produced by R. Collins & Sons in 1899 advertised thirteen wherries and yachts for hire at Wroxham, the wherries costing £9 a week in the late and early season and £10 in the high season, and the single cabin yachts £2 10s and £3. The *Maid of the Mist*, equipped for six persons and with attendant included, could be hired for £4 10s, the *Britannia* with five berths and attendant cost £5 10s and the highest priced yacht was the *Mayflower* with two attendants, at £8 10s.

The pioneer of the hiring business was John Loynes, who in his later years looked every inch the patriarchal figure, with a large spade beard and a yachting cap he was never seen without. Trained as a carpenter, he started to build small boats in Elm Hill, Norwich, in 1878 and was soon hiring them out in response to local demand. Gradually a clientele was built up, but the problem was that the customers were in the habit of sailing the boats round to Wroxham

Broads holidaymakers, Victorian style.

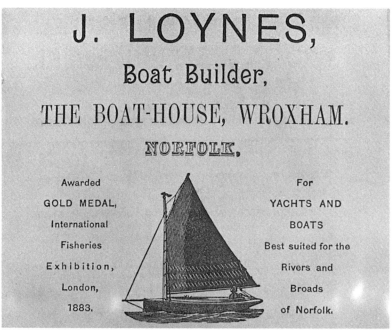

J. LOYNES,

Boat Builder,

THE BOAT-HOUSE, WROXHAM.

NORFOLK,

Awarded

GOLD MEDAL,

International

Fisheries

Exhibition,

London,

1883,

For

YACHTS AND

BOATS

Best suited for the

Rivers and

Broads

of Norfolk.

Mr John Loynes, the pioneer of the Broads boat-letting industry. He started his yacht hiring business in Norwich in 1878, moving to Wroxham shortly afterwards.

and leaving them there, whence they had to be trundled back to Norwich by cart. Loynes therefore soon transferred his activities to Wroxham, where he at first met with a good deal of ridicule and disbelief. Starting with "day sailing" to points at which bed and board could be obtained, he subsequently added canvas covers to his craft, so that his customers could sleep on board. Finally he graduated to cabin yachts. He features in Suffling's book with a full range of cabin yachts and was exhibiting at the Fishing and Yachting Exhibition at the Imperial Institute in 1897.

Another well-known name in the yacht-hiring business was George Applegate. Born in 1824, he came from a family of marshmen and started by watching his father's nets. He took his first employment with a Captain Allington, an inveterate Broads sailor and wildfowler in the middle years of the nineteenth century. Applegate then turned to reed cutting and rush work, and by his early twenties was operating a wherry, the *Olive Branch*. He then rented the lease of Whiteslea and Heigham Sounds for some thirty years, using them for reed cutting and eel fishing. In the closing years of the century, when the railway reached Potter Heigham, he saw his chance in the boat-hiring business and was one of the first to cater to the growing numbers of visitors.

Another turning point was reached in 1907 when a party of six Londoners applied to the railway company for a list of boatyards

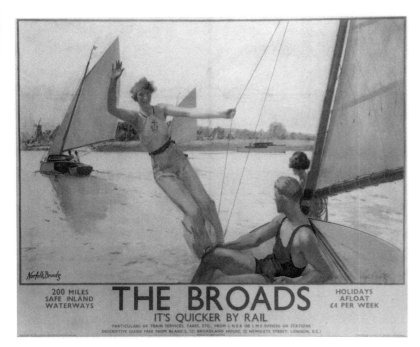

"*It's quicker by Rail.*" *A pre-war advertisement for a Broads holiday.*
National Railway Museum, York

and eventually hired the yacht *Olive* from Ernest Collins in Wroxham. Finding the arrangements more than a little haphazard, one of the party, Harry Blake, offered at the end of the holiday to become Collins' agent in London. So started Blake's Norfolk Broads Holidays, with a 1908 catalogue of forty-three cabin yachts offered for hire for a six-week season. From then on there was no looking back, and what Professor C. E. M. Joad was later, from a lofty height, to castigate as the "untutored townsman's invasion of the countryside" went, in the Broads context, from strength to strength. In 1895 several steam launches were already available for hire, among them the *Falcon* with accommodation for six persons. It was not long before the wherries *Darkie* and *Red Rover* had been fitted with engines and the day of the power craft had arrived.

The years between the two world wars saw a substantial increase in the boat-hiring business, featuring both motor craft and yachts. One of the principal influences, both at that time and subsequently, was Arthur Ransome, who had the happy gift of creating tales of sailing adventures on the Broads and elsewhere with which young people could readily identify. The number of Broads holidays for which he has been responsible must be legion. Immediately before the Second World War around a hundred thousand people were taking them each year.

77

PART TWO

THE LOCUST YEARS

The Environmental Catastrophe: the Rivers, Broads and Fens

7

There will be nothing to attract tourism, including boat hiring, in a degraded and sterile environment . . . As recently as the 1950s and even the early 1960s you could go along in a punt and the water was always gin clear . . . In the late 1960s and 1970s the Broads looked like mulligatawny soup but now there are many which look like tomato soup. My belief is that that is due largely to drainage rather than to pollution from boats . . . It is absurd to say that agriculture, boating or anything else can exist without conservation of that environment.

Lord Buxton of Alsa

If there has been one consistent observation which can be traced throughout Broadland literature, it is that within the living memory either of the author or of the people about whom he was writing there had been an observable deterioration in the Broads environment. In the earlier stages, the observations were often of a diminution in the Broadland fauna, which was generally put down to the depredations of the sportsman, the egg-collector or the professional hunter. Much of the loss was also attributed to the drainage of the marshes, which was given impetus by the development of agriculture following the various Enclosure Acts of the early nineteenth century. Writing in 1845, the Reverend Richard Lubbock was already moved to observe:

Since I first began to sport, about 1816, a marvellous alteration has taken place in Norfolk, particularly in the marshy parts. When first I remember our fens they were full of terns, ruffs and redlegs, and yet the old fen-men declared there was not a tenth part of what they remembered when boys. Now, these very parts which were the best, have yielded to the steam engine, and are totally drained—the marshes below Buckenham, which being taken care of were a strong-hold for species when other resorts failed, and are now as dry as a bowling

79

green, and oats are grown where seven or eight years back, *one hundred and twenty three* Snipes were killed in one day by the same gun. The Claxton marshes, which formerly were almost too wet, are now as dry as Arabia.

Thomas Southwell was fairly typical in commenting in his 1902 edition of Sir Thomas Browne's *Natural History of Norfolk* that several species of bird—such as the bittern and the hen harrier —which had formerly been common in the Broads marshes had at that time almost, if not completely, disappeared. George Christopher Davies also noted at the turn of the century that "the number of wildfowl remaining, even in so suitable a district, is not by any means so large as formerly". This he put down not only to the draining of the marshes but also to the gradual disappearance of the wildfowl decoys and the consequent growth of areas in which shooting was practised.

As the years went by, concern focused on other aspects of environmental degradation in Broadland. During the first half of the twentieth century two such concerns were the diminution in the sizes of the broads and the changes that were seen to be taking place in their vegetation. In 1952, when Dr Joyce Lambert came to deliver the President's Address to the Norfolk and Norwich Naturalists' Society, it was on these two areas that she focused. Regarding the first, she told her audience that her investigations into the profiles of broads had revealed that their original extents had appreciably exceeded their present-day margins. They also showed, particularly in the case of the Bure broads, that there had been little change in the areas of open water up to the time when the various parishes had been mapped in the course of the Tithe Survey of the years 1839–46. It had generally been supposed that the shrinkage of the broads had been largely the result of neglect and lack of traffic during the years of the Second World War. Dr Lambert pointed out, however, that one need only assume a steady accumulation of organic muds over the several centuries after the various broads had become flooded to reckon that a critical stage had in all probability been reached within the last century; then the water had become shallow enough to encourage the encroachment of reedswamp at their margins. The vegetational succession at the edges of the broads was by that time well understood, the essential point being that as soon as the mud had accumulated to a critical depth it was possible for reedswamp to form. In areas where there was only a slight tidal effect, for example the middle reaches of the Bure and Ant, the succession generally began with a zone of lesser reed mace, with patches of bulrush and burweed, behind which the common reed established itself and became the dominant species. On the more tidal Yare, on the other hand, the broad-leaved sweet-grass was normally the first to gain a hold. The effect overall was that the total area of the broads had diminished, as a result of the spread of reed-swamp, from about twelve hundred hectares to some seven hundred hectares between the eighteen-eighties and the nineteen-forties. By 1980 an aerial photographic survey showed that they had shrunk further, to some 600 hectares, or about half their original area. Within the total, there had been individual variations, Ranworth Broad, for example, having decreased in area from about 57 hectares to as little as 20 hectares between 1840 and 1946, and Barton Broad from 115 hectares to some 66 hectares over the same period.

The water areas had included the dykes cut through the fens in earlier periods to enable boats to carry away the marshland crops, and also the "turf ponds", the flooded remains of shallow excavations where—as we have seen—peat had continued to be dug after the main diggings had been inundated, sometimes up to the end of the nineteenth century. These turf ponds had disappeared fairly rapidly after they had been abandoned, while the dykes had become silted up through disuse. Other commentators pointed out that the encroachment of silt and vegetation had also taken place in the larger channels and dykes with the decline of the wherry trade. As long as this trade had continued, the Great Yarmouth Port and Haven Commissioners had repaired the village staithes and dredged the rivers and waterways, while the wherrymen and reed cutters themselves had upheld the public rights to the navigable channels and ronds. Subsequently, however, the channels had become overgrown, banks and ronds had been appropriated for building sites and private moorings, and the staithes had been allowed to fall into disrepair. For as long as the navigation was important for local commerce and convenience the year round, measures were taken to maintain it, but the work largely lapsed once the only interest was that of the seasonal holiday-maker.

On the question of the vegetational succession, Dr Lambert pointed out that for as long as there had been a thriving marshland economy in the Broads, the natural succession in the 3,250 hectares of unreclaimed reedswamps had to a large extent been kept in check. A critical point was, however, reached around the time of the First World War, when a shortage of manual labour, accompanied by the disappearance of horse-drawn transport, meant that the commercial exploitation of the fenlands went into sharp decline. When this happened and the reed-swamps were no longer periodically cleared, mud and dead plants were able to collect around the roots of the reeds until the surface rose above water level and could be invaded by other plants. The invading species varied from place to place, but were commonly tussock sedge, fen sedge or saw sedge. Where tussock sedge predominated, bush colonization tended to take place on the tussocks, giving rise to an unstable growth of "swamp carr" with many fallen or leaning trees creating a tangle of foliage over a very soft tussocky floor. Fen sedge and saw sedge, on the other hand, put out rhizomes and so formed a thicker and more level base on which bushes and trees could obtain a quicker and stronger hold. In all cases, however, the succession to scrub or "carr", predominantly of alder buckthorn, common sallow and bog myrtle, was inexorable; and this progressed to woodland, dominated by alder, ash, sycamore, birch and sometimes oak, as the ground became drier and firmer. There are now many areas of woodland in the Broadland valleys which it is almost impossible to believe were open broads not many decades ago. As a matter purely of aesthetics this can hardly be objected to, as viewers from the tower of Ranworth church can see for themselves. It does, however, mean the progressive loss of Broadland's characteristic landscape, at least in the middle reaches of the river valleys, upstream of the grazing marshes.

For several decades, an intensification of a complex of environmental problems caused by the deterioration in the water

Carr fen at Ranworth. Once the reedbeds have degenerated into a tangle of carr, the diversity and interest of the flora and fauna markedly decline.
P. A. Ewans

quality of the Broadland rivers has been superimposed on these twin problems of the shrinkage of the water areas and the growth of carr woodland. The former limpid character of the Broads' waters has been well attested in the writings of many authors, not least by George Christopher Davies in the latter years of the nineteenth century:

> While sailing up it [the Waveney], you may see, yards beneath you, the tops of waving weeds and shoals of frightened fish; and the blue of its surface and the white of the waves which rise to the bows and eddy astern, are only paralleled by the blue and white in the sky above . . . Its [Hickling's] water is beautifully clear, and its bottom is of hard yellow gravel, over which shoals of fish scud away as one's boat approaches . . . On some of the shallower and smaller Broads, people amused themselves by chasing the pike, which were easily visible under the ice, until they were fairly run down and turned belly up with fatigue, when a heavy blow on the ice with a stick would stun them until a hole could be cut in the ice to get at them.

Already during that century, however, the growth of the city of Norwich had been leading to the pollution of the Yare. Raw sewage began to be discharged into the river in the early eighteen hundreds and the Whitlingham sewage works came into operation in the eighteen-sixties, prompted by an outbreak of cholera in the city some years earlier. A report of 1875 on the Broads' fisheries notes that just below Norwich, "one half of the river was as black as ink. The pollution was as bad or worse than any I ever examined, and I observed several fish floating around dead." From the early nineteen hundreds onwards the increasing number of hire boats on the Broads was also intensifying pollution, as well as damaging vegetation and stirring up bottom sediments. But the consequences of these various developments, while they were certainly noted—George Christopher Davies, for example, drew attention to the effects of motor-boats as far back as 1883—were not at that time seen as particularly serious, and were far from occasioning any systematic research. It was only in the early nineteen-fifties, around the time when Dr Lambert was delivering her lecture, that an increasing turbidity of the water and a progressive loss of aquatic plants began to cause concern. From his observation point at Wheatfen, Ted Ellis noted the deterioration in 1961:

> In 1935, we had a rich aquatic flora, including water-soldiers, plenty of hornwort, frogbit, various pondweeds and quantities of cowbane floating in the corners. All these have vanished . . . In 1935 the Fen Channel was narrow in many places and apt to become blocked by the floating beds of sweetgrass at times. Now it is wide and clear, and most of the floating grass has disappeared . . . Many of the aquatic molluscs which abounded in 1935 are now comparatively scarce. Even the bird life has changed to some extent.

The causes of the deterioration and their relative importance have been a matter of prolonged and sometimes bitter debate, but a programme of research carried out by scientists at the Department of Environmental Studies at the University of East Anglia, mainly in the late nineteen-seventies, succeeded in establishing beyond reasonable doubt what has been happening and why. The basic cause has been shown to be a process of enrichment or "eutrophication", the stimulation of the growth in the water of a dense population of microscopic plant organisms—phytoplankton algae. These algae have two main effects: they inhibit the growth of aquatic plants, largely by depriving them of light and oxygen, and as they die they form bottom sediments. The loss of aquatic plants in turn means that they cease to anchor the sediments, and so these can be more easily stirred up and shifted downstream, increasing the opacity of the water and accelerating the silting up of the rivers and broads. In the absence of the protection which the plants afford, the pressures exerted by boats and boat wash on the marginal reedswamps and river banks also increases, again causing erosion and sedimentation. A vicious circle of loss of aquatic flora, turbidity and sedimentation is thus set up.

Virtually the first significant research into the effects of eutrophication was carried out in the early nineteen-seventies by two scientists from the University of East Anglia, who established that it was the presence of phytoplankton that was largely responsible for the turbidity of the water. The growth of phytoplankton in turn pointed to the enrichment of the water by essential nutrients, which they speculated might be nitrates and phosphates from agricultural land. They found that eleven broads were eutrophicated to the point of being completely devoid of aquatic plants, while a further eleven had poor plant growth. Five more broads, on the Thurne, had suffered a recent loss of plant diversity, while in only one of those surveyed, Upton Broad, did a well-developed aquatic flora remain. By the late nineteen-seventies, apart from a very few broads which were to varying degrees isolated from the main areas of water, virtually all the aquatic plants had gone. As these were at the base of a food chain, their absence had brought with it a loss of the great variety of insects and small aquatic animals which depended on them for food and shelter; and this in turn had caused a loss of fish and other aquatic fauna. The researchers found that much of the associated animal life had also gone from those broads which had lost their aquatic plants.

Later research made it possible to set a timetable for the eutrophication and silting of the broads and to refine Dr Lambert's theory of progressive sedimentation. A number of cores which were taken from the sediments of Barton Broad and were dated

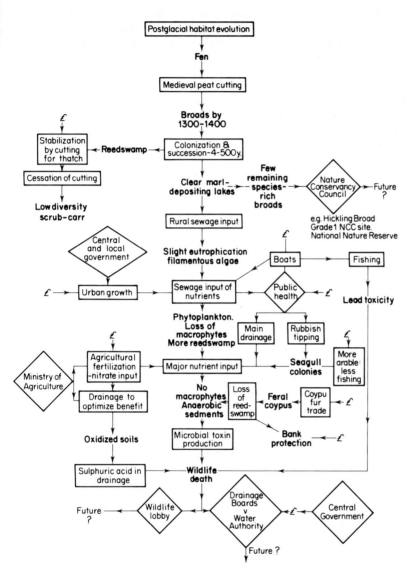

Wetland development and management: an exercise in complexity. This simplified scheme was prepared in 1983; it shows the main features influencing the status of the Broads and their associated wetland margins at that time. Boxes represent causative changes, and bold type consequent conditions. The diamonds indicate legislative or consultative operations at a political level and the £ sign shows economic driving sources or consequences. (Sources mainly Moss, 1980; Ellis, 1965)

mainly by Lead-210 analysis showed that until about 1800 sediments had been laid down on the original peat floor at an extremely low rate. They had increased to some extent in the nineteenth century and rapidly in the twentieth, to a contemporary rate of something approaching a fiftyfold increase over the pre-1800 period. Parallel increases were found in the phosphorus concentrations in the deposits. During the nineteenth century and the first half of the twentieth, the aquatic plant life of the broad had increased substantially, but as the nutrient loading had continued to increase the plants had started to disappear and had eventually been eliminated altogether. In 1911 eleven species of aquatic plant had been recorded in the broad, and ten species had still been present in 1965. By 1972, however, virtually all had gone.

In 1982 an environmental committee set up by the Broads Authority categorized into three phases the process of deterioration of the various broads:

Phase I. The closest to average state between 1400 and 1900. Very clear water, dominated by low-growing plants. Phosphorus levels below 20 microgrammes per litre. Typically, sedimentation less than 1 mm a year.

Phase II. The average state in the period up to the mid-twentieth century. Clear water but with phosphorus levels up to 100 µg per litre. Sedimentation at 2 mm a year. The fertility of the water causes an increased growth and variety of water plants with a proliferation of invertebrates, fish and water fowl.

Phase III. An abundant growth of phytoplankton has coloured the water a murky green and shaded out the aquatic plants. All interesting fauna lost. Levels of phosphorus up to 1,000 µg a litre. Sedimentation rate 1 cm a year.

The committee's analysis suggested that only four isolated broads were at that time still in Phase I and two in Phase II. Three were transitional from Phase II to Phase III and the remaining thirty or so were in Phase III. Since then the deterioration has become even more extreme, and currently only one broad, Upton Broad, is still in Phase I.

The parallel question—and the one which has created the controversy—is what development, or combination of developments, has caused this catastrophic deterioration. At least in the earlier stages, a common presumption, particularly among Broadland residents, was that the main cause of the eutrophication was the great post-war expansion of the hire fleets and particularly of power craft. It was pointed out, correctly enough, that they discharged their sewage in the rivers and broads, they shredded the aquatic plants and stirred up the mud with their propellers, and they damaged the banks either by their wash or by mooring against them, causing silting and turbidity. The growth in the hire fleets, as well as of privately owned craft, was indeed considerable in the nineteen-fifties and nineteen-sixties. In 1946 there were about 3,400 craft on the Broads, about two thirds privately owned and one third hired. About 1,250 of these were powered boats, 1,200 were sailing craft and about 850 were rowing boats of one sort or another. By 1977 the comparable numbers had risen to

*Pea-soup eutrophication (**right,** Ivan West): algae in a polluted dyke as opposed to the Broadland dyke (**below,** Broads Authority): where the limpid water and wealth of water plants, including water soldier, show that this dyke is relatively unpolluted.*

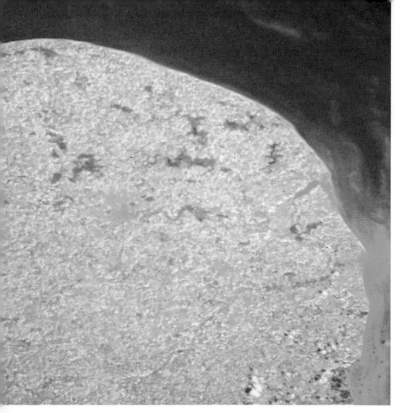

The Broads from space.
This satellite picture
(produced in false colour
format) shows, in pink
colouring, the expanse of
the Halvergate Marshes
and the Broadland river
valleys. Urban areas
appear as light blue,
while Breydon Water and
the broads stand out as
blue or black areas.
Department of
Geography, University of
Nottingham

St Benet's Abbey. Ivan West

some 11,500, about 5,300 of them powered, 3,200 sailing craft (some with auxiliary motors) and 3,000 dinghies and rowing boats. One obvious problem to be tackled, where cruising boats were concerned, was that of sewage. Yet even this relatively simple issue caused endless controversy and took years to resolve. It was not until 1964 that the authority then responsible, the East Suffolk and Norfolk River Board, gave notice that it was proposing new by-laws to prohibit the discharge of sewage and sink water by pleasure craft. The opposition that was immediately voiced by the hire boat owners was as predictable as it was total. They objected to the expense of conversion, maintained that the problem had been exaggerated and predicted even worse problems in disposing of the effluent on shore. But in fact they had already become sufficiently concerned to commission an independent survey by a public health laboratory, which reported early in 1965—much to their relief and satisfaction—that the state of the water over a twelve-month period was "reasonably satisfactory in most places" and that "pollution from boats has not been excessive and has not had a very significant effect on amenities in general". This relief was however short-lived, as a further survey conducted a little later by the local Medical Officer of Health came up with quite different findings, concluding that the rivers and broads were in fact significantly polluted, to the extent that there was a definite risk of people catching enteric fever if they were foolhardy enough to go swimming. It turned out that the incompatibility of the findings of the two reports was due to the fact that the former had been based on water samples taken from the centres of the rivers and broads, while the latter had used samples taken at the margins. Armed with this evidence, the river board proceeded with its by-laws, although it was not until 1973 that all the necessary consultations had taken place, the by-laws had been promulgated and the boats converted. This particular measure, however, while desirable in itself, was far from addressing the fundamental problems affecting water quality, which, it has since been shown, do not in fact derive—at least primarily—from the fleets of boats which make use of the broads. Although their sewage discharge, while it was permitted to continue, no doubt played some part, and although there is also evidence that the boats do stir up inorganic silt from the river beds which remains suspended in the water from day to day, research published in 1977 showed only a weak correlation between boat activity and turbidity, to the extent that the one could not with any degree of probability be said to have been a significant cause of the other. Boats do indeed stir up sediment and erode the river banks, but the material so disturbed is not the major factor giving rise to the sustained turbidity of the water.

A second assumption was that the real culprit was the Norfolk farmer, who accounts for some twenty per cent of the artificial fertilizer which is used in the United Kingdom. The contention here was that a worsening of the water quality can be pinpointed to around the end of the Second World War, when the traditional management of the land gave way to the increasing use of artificial fertilizer. In scientific circles it was, as we have seen, by no means ruled out that eutrophication could be largely explained by the leaching from farmland of phosphorus and nitrogen into Broadland rivers. It was reckoned that this process was likely to have been all the more rapid because the catchments of these rivers, which were areas of intensive arable cultivation, were low lying and had been progressively stripped of their woods and hedges. It seemed probable that the leaching of nitrogen might have begun when these areas first came under the plough and nitrogen was released which had previously been locked up in grazing land. There is, in fact, no doubt that part of the problem does derive from agriculture, but it is much less certain that anything like the whole answer lies in this direction. The first drawback is that while the catchment areas of the Broads rivers stretch far into central and northern Norfolk, the same degree of eutrophication is not in evidence in their upper reaches. The second is that even on the

Holidaymakers at Horsey dyke and windpump, owned by the National Trust.
M. K. Ewans

most generous estimates of likely rates of leaching, it is far from certain that the resulting concentrations would be sufficient in themselves to cause eutrophication to the degree necessary to account for the loss of aquatic plants which has occurred.

The third possibility is that the bulk of the problem has arisen from the discharge of household sewage and detergents into Broadland rivers. In the immediate post-war years there was something of a decline in the population of Broadland and this trend reversed only in the late nineteen-fifties. From that time onwards, the towns and villages in the Broads have all shown a steady increase in population, and there has been a continuing need for new or expanded sewage works, always with the demand exceeding the supply. Even in 1949 the Chief Engineer of the Norfolk Rivers Catchment Board admitted publicly that apart from the Norwich works there was not a single efficient sewage system in the Broads, and that many of the buildings on the river banks discharged their waste directly into the rivers. Between the mid-nineteen-sixties and the mid-nineteen-seventies the population of the Broads area grew twice as fast as it had in the previous decade. The number of houses increased by a third in the same period. The city of Norwich has also grown steadily in the post-war years, with a corresponding increase of effluent being discharged from the Whitlingham works. By the late nineteen-seventies there were fifteen significant effluent outfalls into the main Broads rivers, with a number of smaller ones discharging further upstream. In 1980 a meeting of the Broads Committee of the Anglian Water Authority was told that the effluent from the Whitlingham sewage works and the Cantley sugar factory were far from satisfactory, while half the sewage works in the Broads catchment area were also not meeting the standards set for their discharge, five of them—at Dereham, North Walsham, Diss, Stalham and Wymondham—being particularly bad. Some thirty miles of the Yare, Bure and Waveney had less than acceptable water quality. Not only was the treatment of effluent in the plants in question only partial, but, specifically, there was an incomplete removal of phosphorus, half a kilogram of which is contributed each year by each person using sewage and waste disposal systems. It has been reckoned, in fact, that sewage effluent contains a concentration of phosphorus about a thousand times greater than that contained in run-off from farmland. The concentration of phosphorus—indeed of any nutrient—in a river system can be calculated by reference to the original loading rate, the extent to which the nutrient so introduced is carried away downstream and the extent to which it is deposited in the river sediments. Very little is even now known about the movement of water in the Broads system, but it is certain that the rate of flow of the rivers, while variable from area to area, is generally slow and inhibited to differing degrees by tidal action. This means that flushing action is by no means vigorous and the concentration of phosphorus and its deposition in the bottom sediments is relatively great.

The research undertaken in Barton Broad looked at the development of the two sewage works, at Stalham and North Walsham, that discharged into the River Ant. It was found that the evidence of increased eutrophication and sedimentation corresponded, to an extent which could not have been accidental, with enlargements in the capacities of the works over the years. The researchers suggested that the progressive increase in the deposition of these phosphorus-rich sediments might be correlated first with the introduction of more intensive agriculture during the nineteenth century, and then with increases in the sewage loading from centres of population upstream. The measure of eutrophication in Broads rivers in fact corresponds realistically with what might be expected from the profiles of these rivers and the effluent outfalls into them. The intensification of agriculture, on the other hand, would have been likely by itself to have enriched the Broadland waters only to the extent of accounting for the Phase II richness in aquatic flora. In Barton Broad, for example, it was estimated that while some sixty per cent of the nitrogen was derived from agricultural run-off, only twenty per cent of the phosphorus was derived from this source. In the last analysis, the cause of the deterioration in the water quality of the Broads lies in the increasing pressures of population in the surrounding area.

Subsidiary problems have also appeared. One is a loss of reedswamp and a deterioration in the quality of reed. In recent decades there has been a reversal of the process of encroachment of reed and carr into open stretches of water, and a major loss of reedswamp has occurred. Barton Broad, for example, has lost something approaching ninety-eight per cent of its former margins of reed and reed mace. This was at one time thought to have been mostly due to grazing by coypu, a rodent which escaped from fur farms in the nineteen-thirties and whose numbers escalated in the nineteen-fifties until decimated in the harsh winter of 1962–63 and virtually eliminated by a subsequent campaign of control. But the coypu is now seen by many researchers as no more than an incidental problem and other, more fundamental, causes are generally agreed to be behind the regression of the reed. Primarily, it is thought to be due to the passage into the Broads waterways of agricultural nitrogen, which is known to weaken root growth in plants when it is present in excessive quantity. The loss of reed has in turn exposed the banks to the effects of wash from boats. The banks have also been weakened as a result of dredging, which has

often removed the gently shelving banks on which the reed could gain a footing. Reed has been damaged as a result of grazing by geese and other wildfowl which have lost the aquatic plants on which they had previously subsisted, while trampling of the banks by anglers and others has also been a contributing factor. The tragedy is that as the reeds have been lost on the river margins and bank erosion has intensified, so increasing stretches of river have had to be protected with piling, giving them a wholly unattractive, canalized appearance. A survey carried out in 1980 revealed that only about thirty per cent of the Broads river system was undamaged, while forty-three per cent was eroded and twenty-seven per cent already piled. Taking the Bure and Yare alone, the situation was much worse: twenty-eight per cent of the Bure was piled and sixty-two per cent eroded, leaving only ten per cent undamaged. The comparable figures for the Yare twenty-nine per cent, fifty-six per cent and fifteen per cent.

There is little doubt that eutrophication has been the partial cause of large-scale fish kills and avian botulism in the Broads area. The system of broads that lies at the head of the River Thurne, which includes Hickling Broad, Martham Broad and Horsey Mere, is different from the remainder in that the water is relatively brackish. Although they do not receive any sewage effluent, these broads have become eutrophicated, partly by increased amounts of nitrogen from the more efficiently drained agricultural land, but also almost certainly as a result of their being used for some years as a roost by a large number of black-headed gulls. Already in the

The coypu. An escapee from fur farms, this animal proliferated in Broadland until exterminated by a campaign of control and the harsh winter of 1963. Widely blamed for the loss of reedbeds, it was probably a less significant culprit than was generally supposed.
Norfolk Naturalists' Trust

91

Less attractive aspects of the Broads. The Cantley sugar beet factory on the Yare with Langley dyke in the foreground. The piling of the bank, to protect it against the wash and friction of boats, has become an increasingly common feature of the Broads scene.
P. A. Ewans

nineteen-fifties some 25,000 were counted there, and the numbers subsequently grew, the birds being attracted by the increasing area of arable land and urban rubbish tips. The decline of the North Sea fisheries also meant that they were no longer attracted to the coast. Even before they became a problem, there were records of fish kills in the Thurne system from as long ago as 1894. A particularly serious outbreak occurred in the summer of 1969, when some 250,000 fish including pike, perch, roach and eels were found dead. Further outbreaks were recorded the following spring and in most years thereafter. The cause has been identified as an increase in populations of *Prymnesium parvum*, an alga that grows in brackish water and can produce a toxin fatal to fish. Research has suggested that although an enriched system is not critical and the earlier fish kills could have been caused by *Prymnesium* before the water became eutrophicated, nevertheless there is a link between the size of the *Prymnesium* population and the degree of eutrophication (although the alga does not apparently occur in water which is either too salt or too contaminated by phosphorus). The Thurne area was at one time a favourite with anglers, particularly for pike.

While no fish kills have occurred there in the past few years, yet another Broads tragedy, from a recreational as well as from an environmental point of view, is that this fishery has been largely ruined. Apart from the pike, tench and rudd have almost totally disappeared. The situation has, moreover, had implications for coarse fishing more generally across the Broads.

An additional cause of fish kills has been the periodic salt tides that are apt to flood up the Broads rivers when high tides coincide with a North Sea surge driven by north-westerly winds. Such surges were recorded in 1925 and 1969, and the most recent occurred in 1988, when some 100,000 fish were killed in the Thurne system. These kills were never catastrophic as long as there was a fish refuge in the upper Thurne, beyond the limits of salt water penetration, from which stocks could be replenished. The absence of such a refuge (although fresh water is being pumped into Hickling Broad in order to provide a small one), together with the other pressures on the fish populations across the Broads—notably the loss of aquatic plants and their associated fauna—has now reduced to minimal levels the size and numbers of the coarse fish which at one time made the Broads a fishermen's paradise. As recently as 1963, 53,000 seasonal licences were issued by the river authority, together with 23,000 day licences. Serious anglers these days find it more worthwhile to take themselves off to the nearest reservoir.

A further consequence of eutrophication has, from 1969 onwards, been periodic outbreaks of avian botulism, a paralytic disease which derives from a bacterium, *Clostridium botulinum*, that secretes a toxin and multiplies in warm weather in the type of deoxygenated mud produced under eutrophic conditions. It is now present in virtually every area of the Broads and has caused the widespead deaths of birds. Over a thousand waterfowl, for example, were killed by it in 1975 and 1976. More recently, the eutrophication of the Broads has combined with low water levels and warm summers to produce *Cryptosporidium*, a toxic blue-green alga which is a direct human health hazard. No fewer than twenty-five broads and other stretches of water were found to be contaminated in 1989 and warnings against swimming and water sports had to be isued in both 1989 and 1990.

As if all this were not enough, water quality in the Broads has also been adversely affected by three other external factors. One is the perennial problem of the accidental leakage of livestock slurry. The Anglian Water Authority were provoked by two incidents on the River Yare in the course of 1988 to protest at the low levels of fines imposed on the offenders, each being fined £200 as against the maximum fine of £2,000. In 1990 the Broads Authority drew some comfort from the fact that the number of pollution incidents on the Waveney had fallen from twenty-seven in 1984 to fourteen in 1988, a result of a campaign of warnings and legal action. But fourteen incidents are still a disgrace and the problem seems bound to persist in the absence of adequate sanctions. Another cause for concern is that the deep drainage of acid sulphate soils that has been undertaken in some areas of Broadland—particularly in the Upper Thurne area—has resulted in the development of acidity and the discharge of ferric hydroxide into the waterways. There are few uglier sights than that of a dyke contaminated by a long slick of red "ochre". Less obvious and quantifiable is the effect on the Broads of acid rain. According to a report by the Nature Conservancy Council (NCC—now English Nature), acidification is becoming a problem from which Britain is itself suffering as well as one which it is exporting to Scandinavia. It is probable that since they rely less on rain water and more on spring-fed water sources, the broads are less at risk from this particular source of pollution than are lakes elsewhere. But the effects are unlikely to be negligible. Finally, where fen is concerned, yet another problem has been caused by land drainage, which, by lowering the water table, has drawn water from neighbouring areas of fen and and has not left them enough to keep them in a healthy and flourishing state.

Brograve's Mill (dating from 1771) and the electric pump that has replaced it at Waxham New Cut. The dyke is coloured red-brown from the ochre pumped into it from the marshes beyond.
M. K. Ewans

94

The Environmental Catastrophe: the Landscape and the Grazing Marshes   8

> What sort of uproar would there have been if Norwich cathedral had been taken down, wing by wing, over a period of decades? Yet in the nearby Broads a manmade masterpiece of similar age has been destroyed with hardly a murmur of protest.
>
> The Broads are still a dramatic landscape. It is a flat and silent place, arranged under vast skies, its horizons picked out by spare details—a lonely church, a derelict windpump, a restored red-sailed wherry. But its beauty is a deceit which does not stand up to scrutiny.
>
> *The Sunday Times*

Additionally to the problems of the shrinkage of the broads, decline in water quality and erosion of banks, Broadland has—particularly in the post-war years—been faced with a progressive deterioration of its wider landscape qualities. Soon after the Broads Authority was established in 1979 it appointed a Landscape Working Group to advise it on this aspect of its responsibilities. The working group's method of procedure was first to define a number of Broadland landscape types, following categorizations that had been set out in previous studies, and then to assess the extent to which each had retained its essential character or become degraded. The soundness of this approach was rapidly demonstrated during the Halvergate saga (dealt with in later chapters), since the authority was able to take a stand not on criteria of natural beauty—which might be held to be largely subjective—but on a simple measure of the extent to which the traditional Broads landscape would be damaged by the drainage proposals that were being put forward.

The working group started by formulating definitions of three main types of Broads landscapes, "enclosed", "open valley" and "open flat". Of the "enclosed" landscapes, it put the upper reaches of the Bure, Ant and Yare, along with the Trinity Broads, into a

"fully enclosed" sub-category. This was described as being distinguished by broads and meandering rivers enclosed by reed-
beds, alder carr or field trees, varied by village and holiday
development, all in a fairly narrow river form with cottage and
farm groups and churches often visible on the rising ground. The
other sub-category, described as "less enclosed", comprised the
Upper Waveney and the Chet. This area retained a distinct valley
form, but was on a larger scale and was dominated by grazing
marsh. "Open valley" landscapes were found in the middle reaches
of the Bure/Ant/Thurne complex and of the Waveney and Yare.
Here the valley floor was wide and flat, grazing marsh was
dominant, fewer trees were noticeable, long river lines were
prominent, there were fewer broads, carr and reed-beds, and
windpumps were beginning to be significant. Of the "open flat"
landscapes, there were again two sub-types. One, described as
"open", comprised the upper-Thurne system, with wide stretches
of water, extensive areas of reed, and grazing marsh away from the
main water areas. The other, categorized as "extensive open",
consisted of the large areas of the lower Broads rivers. Rising land
was normally distant, vast open extents of grazing marsh were
prominent and open water was, apart from Breydon, not characteristic.

Having categorized the various types of landscape in this
fashion, the working group then proceeded to divide them into
"landscape units", each in some way visibly distinct from its
surrounding areas. They then assigned each unit to one of four
grades, depending on the extent to which each had retained its
essential features or had to some degree been degraded. They
were careful to emphasize that they were not attempting to assign
gradings in terms of landscape beauty, but in terms of the extent to
which they remained characteristic of the landscape type to which
they belonged. The grades were:

Grade 1. Land of exceptional Broads landscape significance. The best
of the traditional man-made and natural landscapes. No intrusive
development.

Grade 2. Land with typical features, but not as outstanding as Grade 1.
Possibly intrusive pylons or buildings, improved pasture, or small areas
of arable.

Grade 3. Land lacking a positive and consistent Broads character.
Intrusive features and/or considerable areas of arable.

Grade 4. Land with no positive Broads character. Prominent eyesores
and/or extensive arable.

While this may sound a rather complicated and to some degree
arbitrary method of proceeding, it did at least formalize the

situation and establish the basis for a policy which was badly needed at that time. What was disturbing about it was the extent of degradation of the traditional landscape which it revealed. Of about 21,000 hectares of land and water altogether, fewer than half, about 9,500 hectares, were found to be in Grade 1. A further 5,000 hectares were categorized as Grade 2, while not far short of a third of the total, about 6,500 hectares, were assigned to Grades 3 and 4. A particularly disturbing feature of the classification was that many of the most degraded areas were in what might be described as the "heartland" of the Broads—in the river valley between Acle, Ludham and Potter Heigham; in the middle reaches of the Yare valley between Cantley and Rockland; in the Waveney valley below Beccles; and in the lower Bure and Yare around Breydon Water. These were mostly areas of former grazing marsh.

The Broads grazing marshes are a very special part of England's agricultural heritage, unrivalled by any other area in terms of their extensiveness. As we have seen, they were a major feature of the Broadland scene even before the time of Domesday Book, when they were already carrying substantial numbers of sheep and cattle. Extending over the flood plains of the Broads rivers, they no doubt spread during the period when the sea receded, and threatened to diminish as the relative sea level gradually rose from the fourteenth century onwards. In order to preserve the grazing, the marshmen were compelled over the centuries to raise sea walls and embankments and to dig dykes and drains in an endless struggle against encroaching tides and surges. As early as 1101 there is a record of the river bank at Acle being repaired, and it may well have stood for many years before then. New marshes were also enclosed and reclaimed from mudflats and saltings, the meandering dykes often following the courses of former creeks. Each winter, much of the grazing would be inundated, but the land would be enriched each spring by the silt left behind by the receding waters. Sluices were constructed to allow excess water to run off, while protecting the land from the effects of high tides. There is a record of 1617 of the appointment by a manorial court of a number of "fen reeves" to manage the marshes, including the "walls, ditches, drains, sluices, gates, bars, fences and other necessaries". The struggle became easier with the introduction of windpumps from the seventeenth century onwards. Then much of the excess water could be lifted into the drainage dykes and rivers, but the marshes were still liable to be flooded during the winter and spring as well as during periods of calm weather. Drainage boards were later established to organize flood protection and drainage, and land holdings were amalgamated and new windpumps constructed. But as the land was drained, so it shrank below the tidal levels and the risk of flooding was always present. Writing in 1929, Arthur Patterson recalled having witnessed two breaches of the Breydon wall under the pressure of abnormal tides and gales, and of having seen whiting and flounders swimming in the dykes, which remained saline for a long time after the wall had been repaired. By dint of constant management, over the centuries a rich tapestry of grazing marsh was created, which came to cover some 15,000 hectares of the Broadland river valleys. According to the Pagets in 1834, "By the

Victorian steam drainage. This steam pumping engine was built around 1870 and was used for land drainage on Haddiscoe Marshes.
M. K. Ewans

improved banking of the rivers, marshes formerly inundated, are now laid dry, and by the drainage so universally and effectually carried on, deep bogs are constantly, though slowly, converted into the finest and most fertile fields." By 1979 well over a third of this grazing marsh was found by the working group to have lacked "a positive and consistent Broads character".

What makes this situation all the more tragic is that if the visitor to Broadland is asked to describe what, purely in terms of landscape, he believes gives it its uniqueness, it is unlikely that he will first call to mind the narrow valleys of the upper rivers with their enclosures of carr, rising farmland, villages and riverside developments—the first category identified by the working group. The archetypal Broads landscape is rather that of the meandering rivers of the lower valleys, the long views over the grazing marshes, the white sails of yachts apparently sailing across the fields at Thurne Mouth, the windpumps on the river banks, and the great expanses of Breydon, Hickling and Horsey amid their marshes and reedbeds. It would be an exaggeration to say that these landscapes *are* the Broads, the charm of which lies precisely in the variety of its landscape forms, but it its certain that without them the Broads would lose the greater part of the aspects that give it is distinctive character. It would be pleasant to be able to record that the expanses of grazing marsh and their accompanying landscape have been faithfully preserved. The contrary is, however, the case. It was not until the Halvergate controversy brought the whole issue to the fore that any attempt was made to inhibit unsympathetic agricultural development or to discourage the conversion of the grazing marshes to arable, a process which had profoundly altered the character of the open valley landscape. When the Broads Authority came to publish its Broads Plan in 1987, it had to record that some five thousand hectares of former grazing marsh were by then in arable use.

Other threats to the Broads landscape have developed over the years. The working group drew attention to one of them, that of chalet and commercial development, particularly boatyards, along the river banks, all displaying in the working group's words, "no sympathy for Broads character at all". Where chalets are concerned, the stretch of water at Potter Heigham is perhaps the most notorious. Much opposition was voiced when the first of the chalets were being built there in the nineteen-twenties. It was contended that builders had no more right to erect them there, the foreshore being legally a part of the river, than they had to construct buildings on roadside verges. But it does not seem that the question was ever tested in the courts. The Drainage Commissioners and the local authority were no doubt—as was alleged—glad to receive the additional rents and rates which

Bungalosis at Potter Heigham. For at least a mile each side of Potter Heigham bridge the Thurne is disfigured by chalet and bungalow development that was started, probably illegally, in the 1920s.
P. A. Ewans

accrued. The East Norfolk Catchment Board and the Norfolk Town Planning Committee were still looking at the problem in 1936, and, while opposing in principle further development on the ronds, they agreed to consider each case "on its merits". As a result of this and other development, particularly at Wroxham and Horning, some twelve kilometres of river bank had been developed by the early nineteen-eighties, including five, or twenty-five per cent, of the Thurne.

An even more serious threat began to appear in the nineteen-sixties. The problem was that the post-war holiday boom had by then produced a situation in the Broads and neighbouring coastal areas in which facilities for further expansion were seen as urgently required. Several of the companies that had been responsible for the spread of caravan and chalet developments along the coast were starting to look inland, while something of a saturation of the hire cruiser business was causing hire firms to look in the direction of land-based holiday accommodation. Within the space of just a few years, a succession of applications for holiday developments in Broadland hit the desks of the planning authorities. They included proposals for marinas and "holiday centres"—including such facilities as "boatels", apartment blocks, restaurants, caravan sites and amusement parks—and they covered riverside sites at Acle, Horning, Breydon, Burgh Castle, Burgh St Peter, St Olaves and Beccles. Even more ambitious was a £50 million proposal to dredge the mudflats on Breydon and create a series of islands on which would be constructed not only a marina but also a complex of shops, hotel, restaurant, open-air theatre, chalets, stadium, sports centre and helipad. (Smaller islands were however designated as "wild-life reserves".) On a lesser scale, caravan and houseboat developments were proposed for Barton and Hickling Broads, while in 1972 Yarmouth Borough Council proposed that a one-and-a-half mile stretch of marsh on the north bank of Breydon Water should be used as a refuse tip.

All this clearly represented a crisis point for the Broads and it is not difficult to imagine what would have happened if no brake had been put on this sudden pressure for commercial development. It was therefore fortunate that the Broads Joint Advisory Planning Committee was by that time in business. Although this committee had no powers of its own and could only advise the planning authority responsible, its views were influential. It advised rejection of all but two of the proposals, those at St Olaves and Burgh Castle. In those cases, the thought seems to have been that there was an argument for diversifying boating pressures from the northern to the less crowded southern broads. However, the threat of inappropriate and unsightly development has not gone away, and planning applications large and small continue to drop into the Broads Authority's in-tray. One particular application left over from the nineteen-sixties has been for the development of a multi-million pound marina and holiday development on the Waveney marshes at Beccles. Fortunately, the authority has been determined to resist this application and has ultimately been successful in doing so. Another rearguard action has had to be fought—so far successfully—over Stalham staithe. The authority has thus provided good evidence of its sense of its responsibilities, but the pressures are such that it is too early to say to what extent it will manage to keep intact what remains of the Broads' essential landscape and amenity value. A particularly unsightly development has been that of caravan sites in the close vicinity of the ancient monument of Burgh Castle, where permission for more caravans continues to be sought.

★ ★ ★

PART THREE

THE CONSERVATION CAMPAIGN

The Voluntary Conservation Movement

9

The creation of nature reserves mirrors the pattern of the whole concern for conservation in this country. Victorian industrialisation and its concomitant urbanisation, limited though they were in a real extent, alerted the attention of pioneers . . . In Edwardian times came a quickening interest in ecology, the study of plants and subsequently animals in their habitat as such, rather than as isolated specimens . . . Between the wars concern and voluntary action gained impetus, spurred by the rapid extension of the urban area, by increased afforestation and by agricultural change. In 1926, the Norfolk Naturalists Trust was created. This was the first of the County Trusts whose full flowering was to come thirty years later, and which are not simply local natural history societies, but have as a primary object the acquisition and management of local nature reserves.

J. Allen Patmore

If there has been one encouraging development in the long saga of the deterioration of the Broadland environment, it has been the realization on the part of local and national conservation bodies both that problems were developing and that voluntary efforts were needed if, in the absence of any significant governmental or local authority activity, some measure of conservation was to be achieved. The first tentative steps were taken as long ago as 1888, when in order to enforce the Wild Birds Protection Act and stop the indiscriminate shooting of rare birds on Breydon Water the Breydon Wild Birds Protection Society was formed. This society maintained a warden on Breydon for a number of years and was finally amalgamated with the Norfolk and Norwich Naturalists' Society's Wild Birds Protection Committee in 1922.

A much more far-reaching development, however, was the formation of the Norfolk Naturalists' Trust (NNT), thanks largely to the foresight and enthusiasm of Dr Sydney Long, who was house physician at the Norfolk and Norwich and Jenny Lind Hospitals and a keen birdwatcher and naturalist in his spare time. This was by a long way the first of the county naturalists' trusts. It did not escape the scepticism that greeted the nature reserves movement, which was seen in some circles merely as an "attempt by a few rather eccentric sentimentalists to safeguard a hobby", but its reputation grew as it progressively acquired and managed some key wildlife areas, among them Starch Grass and Alderfen in the Broads. Perhaps its most outstanding achievement was the acquisition of Hickling Broad, which remains one of its principal "flagships". We have seen in an earlier chapter something of Jim Vincent's work at Hickling, which he continued to manage under Lord Desborough until they both died in 1944, at which time the NNT acquired the Hickling estate together with the lease of an adjoining area. Four hundred acres of the reserve are open water, while the remaining 960 acres consist of extensive reed-beds and open marshes. Hickling was declared a National Nature Reserve (NNR) during the nineteen-fifties and together with Martham Broad and Horsey Mere (the latter owned by the National Trust) has been recognized as a wetland of international significance under the terms of the Ramsar Convention. This, the Convention on Wetlands of International Importance especially as Waterfowl Habitat, was adopted at a conference held in Ramsar, Iran, in 1971 and ratified by the British government in 1976. As well as Hickling and Horsey, the Bure Marshes have been designated by the government as a Ramsar sites, and an area on the River Ant is likely to follow. The articles of the convention are mostly exhortatory, but they do at least imply a recognition by governments of a duty to ensure the proper conservation and management of designated areas.

Hickling has therefore been a nature reserve for some eighty years. As elsewhere, its management was for a long time little more than minimal, since it is only in the last fifteen to twenty years that it has been accepted that reserves cannot just be left to natural processes but have to be positively managed. Active management of the whole Ramsar site is now practised by the NNT, with support from English Nature. The reed and sedge is regularly cut and sold, scrub has been removed and mowing carried out, wader pools and hides have been built, and shallow drains have been dug to provide the soft, muddy conditions in which snipe, lapwing and redshank can breed. But the results achieved by management have been mixed. Martham Broad has deteriorated within the space of a few years from its Phase I state to one of Phase II eutrophication. Land drainage has introduced salt into the system and Hickling is very much more saline than it was ten years ago. Sedimentation has increased to the point where it is threatening to become a problem for navigation. Large areas of the reserve have dried out. The periodic fish kills and outbreaks of

avian botulism have already been described, and there is no doubt that the decline in water quality has contributed to a worsening of the quality of the reed, particularly where it has grown near waterways. When Hickling was in Phase II of eutrophication, the growth of water plants was such that a weed cutting machine had to be used each year to keep a channel open through the broad to the Pleasure Boat Inn at its head. Then for many years the water plants disappeared. This enabled boats to reach all areas, stirring up mud in the very shallow broad and disturbing the wildfowl. The NNT claim that there has been a steady, if slow, improvement in the water plants over recent years. Weeds are again appearing, although the growth is unstable and is confined to only a few species. Two of Britain's rarest plants, holly-leaved naiad and *Nitelopsis obtusa*, are growing, the latter after three decades of apparent absence. But many other plants have dwindled or disappeared. Of the fauna, the birdlife generally is varied, although numbers cannot be compared with those of former years. The bittern again bred in 1990, the first time for many decades, but only four are currently present. A number of raptors come and go,

Cutting the reed. Although machines have replaced the scythe, reed is still bundled, combed and tied by hand.
Norfolk Naturalists' Trust

*Norfolk Naturalists'
Trust volunteers at work
at Hickling. To manage
and maintain the Broads,
there has never been any
substitute for manpower.
These days, this has to
include a high voluntary
element.*
Norfolk Naturalists' Trust

and the NNT cite one day in May, 1988, when the reserve contained marsh harrier, red-footed falcon, rough-legged buzzard, hobby, barn owl, kestrel, sparrow-hawk and two ospreys. Wildfowl populations have declined steadily since the 1950s. Hickling's once renowned flock of mute swans has been decimated, probably owing, among other things, to the amount of lead shot and anglers' weights in the water. But a variety of warblers, as well as the bearded tit, nest regularly. The otter, formerly present in some numbers, has for many years been entirely absent. Pike, once plentiful, are now very rarely found. The swallow-tail butterfly is still to be seen, as are other species of butterfly and moth.

It is, therefore, an uneven picture, and it is perhaps going too far to say, as one commentator did in 1988, that "Hickling Broad still *looks* very attractive, but from a natural history point of view, it's had it. There's very little life in it—despite its having been scheduled as an NNR several years ago." But the state of the area is nevertheless sad, considering what it once was and could be again. There is a cure for Hickling Broad—indeed for the Ramsar site as a whole—and several promising measures which are under consideration will be discussed later in this book.

The other Ramsar site in Broadland is the Bure Marshes NNR, a large area of unreclaimed fen stretching along the middle reaches of the Bure and including two of the smaller broads, Ranworth and Cockshoot. The greater part of the reserve, which was once used extensively for wildfowling and decoying, was given by the local landowner, Colonel Cator, to the NNT in 1949. While it still retains considerable interest from the botanical, entomological and ornithological points of view, it has nevertheless sadly deteriorated over the years. Ranworth Broad has lost its plant life and its reed margins, the greater part of the sedge beds for which the area was renowned have become carr and the dykes that were formerly used to bring out the sedge have silted up and become overgrown. But the NNT still manage it actively: the carr is being cleared, the sedge beds are being renewed and the dykes are being restored. The sedge, valued for its length and scent, is cut on a three- to four-year rotation and helps to pay for management. The effect of clearance and restoration has been to encourage rare plants such as the marsh orchid, together with a variety of butterflies and birds including warblers and nightingales.

The most significant development, however, is the renewal of Cockshoot Broad, which had deteriorated over the years to a few inches of cloudy water over an infill of thick mud. Plant life was entirely absent, as were all but a few birds. In 1981 and 1982 the broad was sealed off from the river, the mud was removed by suction-dredge and a dramatic recovery took place in the quality of the water, to the extent that within a few months water plants were

Cockshoot Broad. After the mud-pumping the water is clear and water lilies have germinated.
Broads Authority

once agian germinating. However, there have since been problems in achieving a balance between the fauna and flora of the broad, and algae have again proliferated. The expedient that has now been attempted has been to remove all the fish, so as to give the herbivorous zooplankton, on which they feed, the chance to proliferate and to consume the algae. Then, it is hoped, the vegetation of the broad will again flourish and in turn provide a refuge for the zooplankton, so recreating a balanced, self-sustaining environment. The isolation of the broad has not, by itself, been a complete solution, but the experiment has shown that it is not pointless to speculate that it may be possible to restore the broads to some semblance of their former condition, provided that water pollution can be controlled and enriched sediments removed. The experiment has been repeated upstream at Belaugh Broad and Hoveton Little Broad, both of which are connected to the River Bure. The hope here is that with the installation of phosphate-stripping plants on the upper Bure eutrophication will not recur once the broads have been cleared of sediment. So far this seems to be the case, although a sustained regrowth of water plants has not yet occurred.

The NNT own several other reserves in the Broads among them Alderfen, Upton Fen, Hardley Flood and Barton Broad. Of these, Alderfen and Upton are isolated from the main river network, but this did not prevent the former from becoming contaminated by agricultural and septic tank run-off, and a rehabilitation programme has had to be undertaken. Upton

Broad—which, as we have seen, is reckoned to be the only broad still in Phase 1 and is fed by clear spring water—is a habitat for a number of rare species, including swallow-tail butterflies and seventeen species of damsel and dragonfly, among them the endangered Norfolk aeshna dragonfly. In 1989 the purity of the water was threatened when a neighbouring farmer deep-drained a field on the border of the fen and caused a flow of enriched water to seep into the broad. Complicated water storage arrangements, protected by a legal agreement, have had to be devised in order to restore the situation.

The Royal Society for the Protection of Birds (RSPB) were relatively late on the scene in Broadland, but they too are now playing an active role in three vulnerable areas of the Yare valley. Perhaps the most significant of their achievements has been at the lower end of the river, where they are now responsible for virtually the whole of Breydon Water as well as for 366 acres of the Berney Marshes Nature Reserve on its north-western shore, which they purchased in 1986. The significance of this reserve is that it is part of the Halvergate Marshes, the scene of strenuous conservation efforts in the early nineteen-eighties, an account of which appears in later chapters. By restoring the marsh to the shallow flooded conditions that were prevalent before its widespread drainage, the RSPB have succeeded in attracting a wide variety of waders and wildfowl. Breydon Water has, as we have seen, traditionally been a prime site for birds and still receives a variety of migrants and residents, particularly waders.

Further inland, on the northern bank of the Yare between Norwich and Reedham, is Strumpshaw Fen, a gem of a reserve that was established by the RSPB in 1975 and consists of 450 acres of varied habitats, ranging from mature woodland to grazing marsh, carr, reed-beds and open water. It has been sensitively managed and has improved dramatically since it was sealed off from the main river in 1979 and a pollution-free area of some 270 acres was created. The reed is regularly cut, carr has been cleared and the reserve's 120 acres of meadow are managed in the traditional way, without fertilizers or herbicides. The result is that some four hundred species of plants, many of them rare, have been recorded. Over eighty species of bird breed in the reserve, including the bittern and marsh harrier. Buckenham Marshes, a short way downstream, is the only site in England where a flock of bean geese regularly winter, together with large numbers of widgeon.

There are two other landowning trusts in the Broads. One is the Ted Ellis Trust, which manages Wheatfen. The other is the How Hill Trust, which manages Edward Boardman's house and estate near Ludham as an environmental centre and nature reserve, with emphasis on education. Another trust, based at Earsham near

Bungay, breeds otters for reintroduction to the wild. It has been successful in restoring the otter population in Norfolk as a whole to what it was some twenty years ago, before a sharp decline—thought to be due mainly to the transmission of pesticides up the food chain—set in. In Broadland two couples have been released in the Catfield area and are known to have survived, but the population as a whole is undoubtedly extremely small and fragmented, no traces of otters having been found in the past decade either on the Waveney or on the Yare. But further introductions are planned and the population should grow, subject to adequate control of pollution.

Two further trusts, the Norfolk Windmills Trust and the Norfolk Wherry Trust, restore and maintain examples of these traditional Broads artefacts. The Norfolk Windmills Trust was established in 1963, looks after nine windpumps and is engaged, with funding from the Broads Authority, in a programme of preservation and restoration of a further thirty-four. The Norfolk Wherry Trust was formed in 1949 and restored a wherry, the *Albion*, which had been unrigged and was being used as a lighter. For several years she continued to carry cargoes, but she was never self-supporting and is now used exclusively for summer holiday cruises. She may soon be joined by a second trading wherry, the *Maud*, which had been sunk in Ranworth Broad to protect the bank and is being restored at Upton Dyke. Several pleasure wherries and wherry yachts are still being maintained and sailed privately.

Reintroduction of otters. A female British otter with her two well-grown cubs, photographed at the Otter Trust, Earsham, near Bungay.

English Nature has been active in helping the voluntary conservation societies to protect their reserves. According to evidence tendered to Parliament in 1987, they had also by that time designated twenty-seven SSSIs in the Broads, covering some 5,200 hectares in total, or about a quarter of the Broads Authority area. The scandal is that, as we have seen in the examples of the Upper Thurne reserves and Alderfen and Upton Broads, neither the designation of a Ramsar site, nor that of an NNR or SSSI (several reserves are covered by two, or even all three, designations), has been of use in preventing some form of damage. A revealing debate took place in the House of Lords in 1981, when Lords Buxton and Onslow led an attack on the internal drainage boards (whose activities will be examined in more detail in the later section on the Halvergate affair). Lord Onslow took to task the Happisburgh to Winterton Internal Drainage Board, the organization responsible for the deep dyking of the marshes around Hickling and Horsey and thus the release of "ochre" into the waters of this Ramsar site, NNR and SSSI. Despite the intervention of the Broads Authority, the Anglian Water Authority had taken no action. Lord Onslow also cited cases in which a neighbouring internal drainage board had contaminated both Hickling and Martham Broads. In April, 1981, David Ennals quoted in the House of Commons an admission by the responsible minister that five Broads SSSIs, namely the two Ramsar sites, Upton Broad, Calthorpe Broad and Surlingham Marshes, had suffered damage. Other SSSIs and/or reserves have been damaged in Broadland over recent years, and the process is continuing.

Commendable, therefore, as have been the efforts of the voluntary societies in conserving key areas of the Broads, there has also been a downside to their activities. On the one hand, as has been evident from this account, they have with only a few exceptions been unable to insulate their reserves from the general Broads environment, with the result that these have suffered equally from its degradation. At the same time there has been a widespread assumption that because these reserves are in existence, the wildlife of the Broads is adequately protected and there is no need to restrict recreational and other uses. Marion Shoard has made the point very forcibly, suggesting that in the face of relentless erosion of natural habitats the creation of reserves is "welcomed by farming interests as a way of getting naturalists off their backs", and that it has been realized by naturalists that "the idea of preserving samples of the nation's wildlife in neat ghettoes is just not going to work". The agonizing and long-drawn-out efforts to extend the principle of conservation to Broadland as a whole are described in the following chapters.

The Post-War Battle 10
Lines: Phase One
(1945–1961)

The Broads are included as a unique complex of fens and waterways, which provides unsurpassed opportunities for sailing and boating holidays, a distinctive range of flora and fauna, including many rare and interesting species, and a delicate beauty of landscape, derived from the intergradation of water and land, and the soft colouring of the marshlands under a wide sky. It is difficult to see how this area could be successfully protected and managed without the protection of a national authority. Moreover, as a National Park the Broads area will introduce a valuable element of variety into our scheme; it will be the only National Park in the Eastern Counties; and it has the added advantage of being relatively accessible from London and the Midlands.

Hobhouse Report, 1947

The controversy over the proper way of managing the Broads, which was to continue for a full third of a century following the Second World War, has to be seen in the context of the wider controversy that has surrounded the British National Parks system over the same period.

National Parks were late arriving in Britain. Indeed, thanks largely to the opposition of landowners, they have yet to arrive in Scotland. The first National Park in the United States, at Yellowstone, was established as long ago as 1872. This and other subsequent parks which were created in the United States, Canada and elsewhere were substantial wilderness areas, whose beauty could by means of strict management be enjoyed by visitors without detriment to the natural landscape and wildlife. In Britain, by contrast, where the scale of things was in any case immensely smaller, there was scarcely an environment or landscape that did not already owe much of its character to settlement, agriculture or some other form of human intervention, and there were no large areas that could be set aside purely as nature reserves. Even in the remotest regions there are inescapable conflicts between established land usage, recreation and access on the one hand, and the preservation of the landscape and wildlife on the other. These conflicts have permeated the whole history of our attempts at nature conservation. For many years these inhibitions delayed the creation of a National Parks system, and they have been bedevilling it ever since.

Nevertheless, as realization gradually spread of the extent to which the Industrial Revolution had ravaged the British countryside, so pressures grew for some form of action to preserve what were seen as the most valuable areas left. One of the earliest conservation societies, the Commons Preservation Society, was founded as early as 1865 and was followed by the National Trust in 1893 and the Society for the Promotion of Nature Reserves in 1912. In the years between the two world wars an alliance was formed between the main conservation and countryside organizations, and continuing pressure resulted in the establishment of a committee under the chairmanship of Christopher Addison, then Parliamentary Secretary to the Minister of Agriculture. (It is of some interest that while this committee was deliberating, a plea for a Broads National Park was made, sixty years before it effectively came about, in a book by Dr Vaughan Cornish, *National Parks and the Heritage of Scenery*). The Addison Committee reported in 1931 in favour of the establishment of a National Parks system, but the initiative foundered in the midst of the economic depression. Following this setback, the Joint Standing Committee for National Parks (now the Council for National Parks) was formed in 1934 and became an increasingly articulate and influential lobby. By the time of the Second World War the climate of opinion, strengthened by the more general feeling that there was a need for a radical post-war reconstruction of many aspects of national life, was strongly in favour of a National Parks initiative. This was strengthened by the recommendations of a committee under Lord Justice Scott, set up late in 1941 to advise on ways to protect and develop country areas. One of the Scott Committee's recommendations was that a number of National Parks should be established in which the existing land use (eg sheep farming) should be continued but would "become secondary to the main purpose, which is public recreation". The committee envisaged that nature reserves would be set up as a separate exercise, whether within or outside the National Parks, and that control of access would be a main consideration. There has been much criticism of the Scott Report, not least in that it failed to foresee the development and intensification of farming practices that was subsequently to alter profoundly the face of the countryside, whether in National Parks or further afield. Nor did Scott foresee the vast growth in mobility and recreation that was to exercise such pressure on the relatively "unspoilt" areas of the country. But Scott did at least conceptualize the problems inherent in the formation of National Parks and nature reserves, and he made the first tentative steps to articulate solutions.

The coalition government's response to Scott was to appoint John Dower, a temporary civil servant in the Ministry of Town and Country Planning who was also a keen rambler, to study the National Parks issue further and to produce a report. His definition of a National Park was as follows:

> . . . an extensive area of beautiful and relatively wild country in which, for the nation's benefit and by appropriate national decisions and action,
> (a) the characteristic landscape beauty is strictly preserved,
> (b) access and facilities for public open-air enjoyment are amply provided,
> (c) wildlife and buildings and places of architectural and historic interest are suitably protected, while
> (d) established farming use is effectively maintained.

A wherry on the Bure. Payne Jennings' photograph, taken around 1890, conveys something of the peacefulness of the Broads at that time.

This has been the bench-mark against which all subsequent developments in and over the National Parks have been measured. As far as the Broads were concerned, Dower had some doubts, mainly due to the feeling that a lowland area of rivers and wetland with a relatively intensive agriculture and a developed holiday industry did not fit naturally into the pattern of wilder uplands which he saw as the natural parks environment:

> there are too many complications, both of drainage, navigation etc., and of existing misuses and disfigurements; and the requirements differ materially from those of a regular national park. It may prove better to deal with the area on some *ad hoc* scheme of combined local and national action, which should include the protection of substantial areas of mere and marsh as strict nature reserves.

Dower did, however, put the Broads on a "reserve" list and left open the question of their inclusion.

Dower's report was on the desks of the incoming Labour government of 1945, and their response was to appoint a committee under the chairmanship of Sir Arthur Hobhouse, charged to fill out the Dower recommendations and produce detailed proposals. The Hobhouse Report, which appeared in 1947, was altogether more positive—indeed almost ecstatic—about the Broads. They were, Hobhouse reported

> a potential National Park which seems to belong to another world, so widely does it differ from the mountains and wild moorlands of the north and west, or the rolling contours of the South Downs. Slow rivers creep between its fens and fields. Wide, shallow meres—the Broads themselves—lie along their courses, their edges merging into reedbeds or waterlogged alder carrs. The bank of a dyke is an eminence whence you may see white or gaily coloured sails progressing mysteriously across a meadow; you will see also a few scattered woods, perhaps a derelict windmill or two, an immense stretch of sky, and sometimes, on the far horizon, a pale sliver of sand dunes marking the shore of the North Sea."

Hobhouse concluded that "the Broads have a special claim to selection as a National Park quite apart from their natural beauty; by reason of their holiday and recreational value and the interest of their plant and animal life"; and he expatiated in language which is, to say the least, unusual for an official report about the opportunities for sailing and angling, and the attractions of the flora and fauna:

> Here the bird enthusiast may watch one of the rarest of British birds of prey—the marsh-harrier, and if he has luck and patience may see the spectacular "aerial pass" when the male harrier returns from hunting, calls his mate up from the nest and drops the prey to her as she turns on her back in mid-air to catch it deftly in her outstretched claw.

The charms of the bearded tit are then described, together with those of "that weird member of the heron tribe—the bittern. Its eerie foghorn booming, the shrill whistle of otters and the pig-like grunting of water-rails are characteristic sounds of the Broadland night."

But Hobhouse was also clear about the problems. The most serious of these was the encroachment of aquatic vegetation on the open water, the only remedy for which was clearing and dredging. Inundation by the sea was a danger, as was contamination by salt water and organic pollution. Public right of access to closed broads and waterways would have to be facilitated, while new holiday and boating centres were required, to reduce congestion on the Bure. Staithes and windpumps needed to be repaired and preserved. The number, size and speed of motor-boats should be limited and a considerable increase in the number of sailing craft promoted. All this would entail expenditure on a larger scale than in other National Parks, but this would be fully justified by the increased public enjoyment of "the finest inland sailing waters in the country". Hobhouse also published a map of the proposed area of the Broads National Park. As well as the immediate area of the rivers and broads, this included the stretch of coast between Winterton and Sea Palling as well as much of the surrounding uplands in Flegg and Lothingland and towards the A1151 between Wroxham and Stalham—a total extent of 181 square miles. As for the other proposed National Parks, Hobhouse recommended that a park committee should be set up totalling not more than twenty-five members, half appointed by local councils and half by the National Parks Commission, which should also appoint the chairman.

Meanwhile, at the local level, there was also some immediate post-war activity. Already at that time there were a number of authorities that had statutory responsibilities of one form or another for the Broads area. Although there were reorganizations from time to time, the problems of persuading them to agree to relinquish any part of these responsibilities or to co-operate in setting up a unified Broads regime were to persist for all of thirty years. First of all, there were two county councils, those of Norfolk and East Suffolk. There were also the two county boroughs of Norwich and Great Yarmouth; a number of rural district councils; the East Suffolk and Norfolk River Board, which was responsible for land drainage, coast protection and fisheries; and the Great Yarmouth Port and Haven Commissioners, who were responsible under a succession of Acts of Parliament not merely for the port of Yarmouth but also for most of the navigation on the Bure, Yare and Waveney, which were legally part of the port. The three rivers were, however, administered by separate river commissioners, under the Port and Haven Commissioners' overall supervision. In April, 1945, Norfolk County Council convened a conference of these authorities to consider the future of the Broads. This resulted in the setting up of an investigation committee, which, like the Hobhouse Committee, reported in 1947. Uppermost in the minds of the committee was the realization that the Broads were suffering from a plethora of conflicts and overlaps between the various authorities against a background of almost total neglect during the war years. Until 1943 Broadland had been part of a defence area and visitors had been excluded. Lack of use had resulted in a loss of water space and a deterioration of the infrastructure, while an increase in the number of visitors was now to be expected. The committee pointed to many of the threats described by Hobhouse, the danger of sea floods, the growth of vegetation, the problems of pollution and the lack of "elbow-room" for boats. The committee's preferred solution was that the Broads should be controlled by a single executive authority, but it abandoned this proposal when it was advised that an Act of Parliament would be required for the purpose and that would undoubtedly be opposed by all the existing local councils—if only because it would probably have to be financed locally without any contribution from central government. This advice turned out to be sound, since, when a second conference was held in May, 1947, to consider the committee's report (a conference which was described in the Norfolk press as "to some extent discordant"), it revealed all too clearly the tensions that existed between the local councils and the other authorities. It also had to face the fact that the Hobhouse recommendations and, even more importantly, the government's views on them were at that time unknown and that further uncertainty existed owing to the imminence of legislation to reorganize the river boards nationally. There was thus little constructive local consensus and no general framework in which practical decisions could be taken. The conference resolved merely that a permanent committee would be set up "to reconcile and advise all those involved in the administration of Broadland", but without any statutory or executive powers. One interesting sidelight, however, is that even this purely local conference was at that time prepared to consider boundaries for the Broads area which included even more stretches of upland than those sketched out by the Hobhouse Committee.

There was then a hiatus while the government considered the Hobhouse recommendations, broken only by a debate in the House of Commons late in 1947. Edward Evans, then the Member of Parliament for Lowestoft, took the opportunity of a debate on the adjournment to press for early action. He identified the problems of Broadland as being those of silting, pollution and unlawful enclosure. He was strongly critical of the Broadland local authorities who, he maintained, benefited from some £6,000,000 worth of tourist expenditure each year, while doing absolutely nothing towards the upkeep of the Broads for recreational purposes. This was "nothing more or less than sheer robbery." Following the debate, the Minister for Town and Country Planning, Lewis Silkin, delivered a detailed reply to the points raised. The thrust of this was that the machinery for the solution of the problems of the Broads lay in the proposed establishment of a system of National Parks, but that there was no reason why the local authorities should not co-ordinate their efforts meanwhile, on a non-statutory basis.

Edward Evans returned to the charge in 1949 when the National Parks and Access to the Countryside Bill was introduced. In response, Lewis Silkin said that he had the Broads particularly in mind when including in the Bill specific powers for planning authorities to improve waterways, but he also warned that the Broads posed

> a peculiarly difficult problem. Not only are there the difficulties to which he [Edward Evans] alluded but there are a multiplicity of authorities there. There are harbour authorities which have jurisdiction so far as the tide goes; there are other authorities concerned with river pollution, which is a most vital matter; and there are at least a dozen other bodies concerned with various features of the life of the place.

The government's "steer" over the Broads was thus discouraging and Edward Evans' intervention effectively marked the high-water mark of the immediate post-war pressure, whether within or outside Parliament, for the formal inclusion of the Broads in the National Parks system.

It had been envisaged by Hobhouse that once established the National Parks Commission might take some three years to set up the twelve National Parks, the Broads being among the final group, timed for the third year. Events, however, were to work out otherwise and in fact the commission took until 1957 to produce ten of the twelve parks, and even longer to decide what best to recommend about the Broads. In this lengthy interval, virtually the only development of any significance was the establishment by the two county councils and the Norwich and Great Yarmouth Borough Councils of the Broads Joint Advisory Planning Committee. This committee was widely criticized for its ineffectiveness, and indeed it failed to impinge on policy issues over the whole period of its existence. It was, however, given delegated powers to consider all planning applications in the Broads areaand it at least protected the Broads, as we have seen, from a number of development proposals which would have ruined for ever much of the distinctive character of the region.

Also during the nineteen-fifties came the Bowes Committee on Inland Waterways, which devoted a chapter of its report to the Broads. Sensibly enough, it laid emphasis on the need to tackle the practical problems of dredging and river improvement, but it raised hackles by recommending not only a rise in the levels of tolls but also the levying of a rate on the local councils for the purpose. Even more controversially, it recommended that the Port and Haven Commissioners should be reconstituted on a more representative basis, to include members appointed by the local councils, by boat-owners and possibly by the National Parks Commission and the Nature Conservancy. It also suggested that the administration of the rivers and broads by an authority of this nature might be separated from that of Great Yarmouth port. The waters were then further muddied (if that is the right term) by a proposal from the East Suffolk and Norfolk River Board that it should take over from the Port and Haven Commissioners the responsibility for navigation; and this idea was endorsed, against the strong opposition of the commissioners and boating interests, by a conference of the planning committees responsible for the area. Given this degree of local contention, it was not difficult for the government to insist once more that the question of National

Hickling Broad: a photograph taken in 1945, when the Norfolk Naturalists' Trust acquired Hickling as a National Nature Reserve.
Times Newspapers Ltd

Park status would have to be resolved before there could be any question of legislation for purely local purposes. When a government minister, Lord Jellicoe, was pressed about this in the House of Lords in 1961, his reply was that there was still "considerable local disagreement" on the subject and the government had felt

> a natural reluctance to impose a settlement which would not command broad local acceptance. However, as the Bowes Committee have pointed out, this is a matter of urgency, and my Right Honourable Friend [Henry Brooke, the Minister of Housing and Local Government] recognises that he may have to step in.

In the event, any sense of urgency that might have existed seems to have evaporated quickly and the announcement that came in August of that year said no more than that in the view of the National Parks Commission, "the unique character of the Broads makes them in no way comparable in type with the other areas which, in conformity with the general requirement laid down in the National Parks and Access to the Countryside Act, it has selected and designated as National Parks". The significant features of this announcement are that it appeared merely as a written reply to a parliamentary question and failed to provoke a debate or any other parliamentary response, and that neither the government nor the National Parks Commission appears to have considered that there was any need at all to try to explain or justify the decision. Nor does it appear to have provoked any local reaction, favourable or otherwise.

This rejection of the concept of a National Park marked the end of what might be called the first stage of the campaign for the Broads. Particularly with the benefit of hindsight, it is not difficult to see why the effort ground to a halt. A main reason was that as long as the country-wide initiative for a National Parks system was in play, this effectively put paid to any chances of the emergence of any alternative solution. The government were not prepared to consider "one-off" legislation, and this precluded the formation of a body with all the executive powers that appeared necessary. Nor in any case was there sufficient local enthusiasm. There was a dislike of any "third tier" of local government, there was a reluctance on the part of the local councils to incur any additional expenditure (and Hobhouse had suggested that a Broads National Park would be likely to be the most expensive of all), there was rivalry between the various authorities, none of whom was prepared to contemplate any erosion of its powers and responsibilities, and above all there was very little public pressure for change, whether locally or at the national level. The Broads boating industry was expending comfortably and saw no need for any controls: indeed the suggestion made by the Hobhouse Committee that there might be some restriction placed on the numbers of motor-boats was clearly thoroughly counterproductive in that particular quarter. The conservation trusts seem to have made little impact; the Broads Society, when it came to exist, was totally ambivalent on the issue; and the farmers and landowners wanted none of it. If James Wentworth Day is to be believed, the great majority of local people were opposed to the idea of a National Park essentially on the grounds that it would entail a burden of bureaucracy, imposed from London, on all those who made their living on the Broads and were already running it themselves in a perfectly adequate fashion. This simplistic view, which took no account of the additional resources that National Park status would attract for conservation and amenity purposes, may have derived in part from experience of central government intervention in local affairs that had been a feature of the wartime years. Also the post-war Labour government with its use of planning and other controls was anathema to a staunchly Conservative rural Norfolk. This ingrained insistence on local autonomy persisted, and contributed throughout to the problem of doing something effective about the Broads, even when their deterioration became increasingly obvious as the years went by.

In the final reckoning, however, the Broads were at the end of the queue for National Park status and there were always doubts, first articulated by Dower, about its appropriateness. Some years later, the Countryside Commission ascribed the reasons for the rejection to a belief that the area was too water-based and did not afford sufficient opportunities for land-based recreation; to a feeling of repugnance at the poor quality of riverside development; and to a hope that the Port and Haven Commissioners would cope effectively with the management of the water areas for recreation. These factors may indeed have played some part in the decision, but clearly there was much more to it than that. The fact was that by the time the Broads came to be considered by the National Parks Commission, the bloom had gone from the National Parks concept and there was little disposition to create any more.

★ ★ ★

The Post-War Battle Lines: Phase Two (1961–1975)

The authorities concerned have drifted under the spell of a new Columbus syndrome in which they from time to time "discover" that there are recreational and ecological problems in the Broads without accepting that the problems are worse rather than different, and worse largely because statutory reorganisation has not been effected.

Peter Owen

Like the National Parks Commission, the Nature Conservancy was established in 1949 under the provisions of the National Parks and Access to the Countryside Act. It had its origins in the report of the Wildlife Special Conservation Committee which had been set up under the auspices of the Hobhouse Committee with Sir Julian Huxley as its chairman, and it possessed its own Royal Charter. Its strengths were, first, that it had the responsibility of tackling nature conservation on a scientific basis, which meant that its views could not easily be disregarded; and, second, that it had executive powers that enabled it to acquire and manage nature reserves. It could not, however, readily take a broader view, whether in terms of the conservation of the landscape and the amenities of the countryside generally, or in terms of substantial areas of land, such as National Parks. From the nature of its work, its remit normally comprised only small-scale natural environments. The broad view was the responsibility of the National Parks Commission, which did not, however, possess any executive powers. In Broadland, the Nature Conservancy had in 1959 designated two major NNT reserves as NNRs, the first in the Bure Marshes around Woodbastwick and Ranworth, and the second at Hickling Broad. By the early nineteen-sixties two more NNRs were in prospect and there were also at that time fourteen SSSIs that the Conservancy had designated within the Broads area. These responsibilities led the Conservancy, unusually—but not, it seems, reluctantly—into the wider arena.

The 1961 rejection of National Park status caused much concern within the Conservancy and its response was to undertake a review of the implications for its NNRs and SSSIs. It did not take it long to realize that these implications could not be divorced from the fate of the Broads as a whole, and so it went on to produce early in 1963 a public report which it was careful to describe as "simply a draft for discussion". The Conservancy's thesis was that conflict between the various users of the Broads was growing, that a deterioration in wildlife interest was to be expected and that time was running out if the Broads were to be preserved as part of the national heritage. Although there was some immediate criticism of the report on the part of boat hirers and others, the Conservancy was successful in stimulating serious discussion. It managed the following year to persuade a cross-section of local people representing organizations with interests or responsibilities in the Broads area to form a working party to assist it in looking further into the problems and in making recommendations. The exercise eventually culminated in the *Report on Broadland*, which was published by the Conservancy in July 1965 and was supplemented by a unanimous report by the working party—an outcome that represented a major diplomatic coup for the Conservancy and its chairman, Lord Howick, even if some of the recommendations were, one would have thought, somewhat at odds with its proper concerns.

One of the more curious recommendations stemmed from the Conservancy's perception of the congestion and "conflict between users" in the northern Broads. This led it to propose not merely that existing silted and overgrown broads should be dredged, but that a number of new broads should be created, possibly in the triangle of marshes between the Yare, the Waveney and the Haddiscoe New Cut, or between Oulton Dyke and the Waveney. Other sites mentioned were the Beccles region and the Strumpshaw/Postwick/Brundall area on the Yare. The idea was to create more space, not just for cruising boats, but also for speedboats and water skiers. The report also suggested the creation of new broads on the northern rivers, possibly in the vicinity of Womack Water and at Upton. Even more odd for a body which had as its main responsibility the preservation of the natural environment was the suggestion of a new cut between the Bure and the Yare, to run along the eastern edge of the Halvergate Marshes from the neighbourhood of Stracey Arms to a point east of Reedham (bisecting in the process what is now an SSSI). The cost, which would have had to include two rail bridges and one road bridge and possibly some locks (although the report was not clear on this), was estimated to be of the order of £1 million.

Both the Conservancy and its working party were obviously much concerned at the administrative vacuum left by the closure of the National Park option. They seem to have felt that there was no future in trying to revive that particular issue and so they came up with a proposal that the government should create a new series of National Recreation Areas of which the Broads should be the first, together with an agency to administer them—a concept which, apart from its political naïvety, also came rather oddly from a conservation agency. As interim measures, the Conservancy and the working party proposed various programmes of research and called for a new, co-operative approach on the part of all the responsible authorities, which should be formalized in a consortium under "a person of standing appointed by the Government". As for finance, the solution to this inevitable problem was not so easily formulated and the proposal for National Recreation Areas seems to have represented, in part at least, a somewhat desperate effort to attract government funding.

Despite the evident drawbacks and lack of realism of parts of the Conservancy's report, and although there was in the short term very little to show for it on the ground (and certainly not any new broads or Bure/Yare cut), it was successful in re-creating the momentum lost by the withdrawal of the National Parks Commission. Whatever their real feelings, the organizations whose representatives had constituted the working party found it difficult to repudiate their conclusions. In the course of 1966 the three principal authorities concerned, Norfolk County Council, the Great Yarmouth Port and Haven Commissioners and the East Suffolk and Norfolk River Board, formed themselves into the suggested consortium and each appointed four representatives to the Consortium Committee under the chairmanship of a former Director-General of the Ordnance Survey, Major-General Arthur Dowson. They were joined late the following year by the East Suffolk County Council. The report of the committee, the *Broadland Study and Plan*, had as its basis a "strategic plan" prepared by Richard Maxwell, Chief Planning Officer of Norfolk County Council, which appeared in 1969. As one might expect, this latter document was highly professional in style, well researched and illustrated, and it is perhaps still the best analysis available of the problems and issues at stake. It was, however, criticized at the time for viewing with apparent equanimity a doubling of Broads holiday-makers by the end of the century, without much consideration of the ecological consequences and against the background of a "chaotic traffic jam of craft" on the rivers.

The Consortium Committee proceeded to examine Richard Maxwell's plan and to receive representations on it, and finally submitted its own report early in 1971. Its approach in many ways echoed that of the Nature Conservancy in that one of its main concerns was the congestion on the northern rivers, which it proposed should be alleviated by discouraging altogether the

Congestion on the Broads. A summer day's scene on the Bure.
Eastern Daily Press

expansion of holiday and recreational activities and facilities there and by a more limited expansion of the use of the southern rivers. The committee did not, however, support the idea of a new Bure/Yare cut, which it regarded as unduly expensive for any purpose it might serve. It did propose a cut along the old Hundred Dyke between the Ant and the Bure north of St Benet's Abbey, in an attempt to relieve the river traffic along the Bure between Ant Mouth and Thurne Mouth. It approved the concept of "zoning" water activities throughout the Broads, with the encouragement of sailing and angling in preference to power-boats, and it strongly advocated the adoption of a comprehensive landscape plan to include the restoration of windpumps and the banning of any further static caravan sites. It was strong on the control of pollution, but limited in outlook when it came to conservation issues, advocating the discouragement of damaging activities only in nature reserves and SSSIs.

Finally, the committee again tried to tackle the question of a comprehensive administration for the Broads area. A particular problem at that time was the prospect of the country-wide reorganization of local government, and the committee's recommendations had to be hedged. There was also, once more, disagreement between the various authorities. The County Planning Officer had recommended the establishment of a "new authority" with "overall administrative responsibility" for the area. It should be responsible for navigation outside Great Yarmouth and should be consulted by local planning authorities when the latter exercised their powers "in accordance with an approved overall plan". The authority should consist of not more than twenty-four members, three-quarters representing the various local interests and the remainder "individually nominated". The National Farmers' Union, the Country Landowners' Association and the river authority should be represented on the authority, the latter, however, retaining its responsibility for drainage. These proposals clearly provoked no little controversy within the committee. The river authority proposed an amalgamation with the rivers commissioners to produce the one authority. The rivers commissioners, however, not surprisingly demurred and went on record as preferring a single authority which would include the planning authorities as well, or, failing that, acceptance of the recommendations made by the County Planning Officer. A majority of the committee sided with the river authority, with the proviso that the single authority should also be given "any additional powers to enable them to carry out the plan for the future management and development of Broadland". This provoked the Port and Haven Commissioners to make it known in a subsequent statement that they opposed "in the strongest possible terms" the assumption by the river authority of any responsibility for navigation.

The initiatives of the nineteen-sixties thus collapsed in a welter of disagreement, and the Consortium Committee, taking the view that it had completed its work, wound itself up. Many of those concerned then became involved in various schemes of reorganization which were implemented in the early nineteen-seventies. Following the reorganization of local government, the Broads Joint Advisory Planning Committee was replaced by the Broads Consultative Committee, which like its predecessor was generally ineffective on policy issues while advising the various planning, water and navigation authorities on developmental matters. The water authorities were also reorganized at that time, and the Anglian Water Authority (AWA) was created, assuming the responsibilities for the "water cycle" formerly exercised by the river authorities, the water supply undertakings and the district councils. In response to pressures from local conservation agencies, in 1974 the

AWA formed its own Broads Committee with executive powers for the area. But there was little or no co-ordination between the two committees, and still less joint action in the area of management. Meanwhile the commissioners for the three Broadland rivers were amalgamated to become a single rivers authority. The two national conservation agencies also had other things on their minds: the National Parks Commission had become the Countryside Commission in 1968, acquiring more general responsibilities for promoting conservation and recreation in the countryside; while the Nature Conservancy became the Nature Conservancy Council (NCC) in 1973, with many of its scientific functions transferred to the Institute of Terrestrial Ecology. It was not until 1976 that a fresh initiative was undertaken which was eventually to lead to the establishment of the "purpose-built" authority consistently recommended in the long series of post-war reports that had each, one way or another, been put to one side.

The diminutive "Smock Mill" at St Olave's.
P. A. Ewans

The Broads Authority: Mark I   **12**

In 1978 the Countryside Commission was aware that the root of the problem in the Broads was the need for an authority with new powers but was out-manoeuvred when local statutory organisations closed ranks to recycle their by then well rehearsed "solution" to a potential attack on their own statutory integrity. Now there are four major reports on the Broads and the Broads Authority is a very poor substitute for an authority with new powers.

Peter Owen

During the early nineteen-seventies the process of ecological deterioration in Broadland continued virtually unchecked. The "Columbus syndrome" then re-emerged in the shape of yet another survey, this time by the NNT, which showed amongst other things that the great majority of the broads were in advanced stages of degradation and had lost most of their traditional flora and fauna. This aroused a good deal of concern, and both the Countryside Commission and the NCC were moved to take the situation seriously, the latter setting in train a substantial pro-gramme of research in response to the NNT's initiative. The message delivered by Ian Mackintosh, the President of the NNT, at a meeting called to arouse public awareness of the situation, was stark: "what we are witnessing", he said, "is the death of the Broads." The Countryside Commission, for its part, responded by displaying a sense of purpose in marked contrast to the defeatism shown by the National Parks Commission fifteen years earlier. This was all the more unexpected considering that the Secretary of State for Wales had turned down only a couple of years previously, without even the courtesy of a public enquiry, the commission's designation of the Cambrian Mountains National Park in mid-Wales. Towards the end of 1976 the commission set the ball rolling by issuing a consultation paper "for the purposes of examining the desirability of designating a National Park for the Broads". The commission's tactics were to combine persistence with diplomacy, and it was careful to invite and consider the views of any organization or individual who wished to have a say, at the same time keeping up a momentum and presenting its correspondents with proposals on which they were compelled to comment if they were not to find decisions being taken over which they had exercised no influence. The commission did not itself enter, at least publicly, into the intense local debate that its proposals generated, and it earned a reputation for bureaucratic aloofness which undoubtedly contributed to the eventual rejection of its preferred course of action. But its method of proceeding was probably as such as the local market would bear, and a more vigorous and intrusive attitude might well have led to the collapse of its initiative.

The initial consultation paper set out to explain what would be involved in a National Park designation. It set out the background, stressing the view of the Sandford National Park Policy Committee, which had reported in 1974 with the endorsement of the Department of the Environment that there was a need for further National Parks with more diverse landscapes and a more even geographical distribution. It was careful to stress that there was no firm intention to proceed with designation but that an opportunity was simply being offered for everyone to say what they would like to see put in place. Having thus lit the blue touchpaper, the commission retired and waited for responses.

These were on the whole predictable. Norfolk County Council started off by accepting the principle of a National Park on the conditions that its governing body should be a committee of the council and not an independent planning board, that there should be agreement on the precise boundary and that they should be consulted about the appointment of a chief executive. Subsequently, however, the council took the view that there ought to be consultation about the possibility of establishing a special form of organization for "what was essentially a water-based area". Suffolk County Council was also in favour of a single Broads authority, not necessarily on the National Parks model. The district councils were altogether more negative. None of them wanted a National Park, partly because they did not think that it would be likely to have enough power over water pollution and navigation, and partly because they were afraid that it would encourage a further growth of tourism—particularly of the land-based variety—which the Broads would not be able to accommodate. The district councils were also sceptical about "another tier of local government" that would cost money and duplicate and delay planning and other procedures. Although not explicit, there was certainly also no little fear on the part of the councils that many of their powers might be siphoned off to the benefit of the county councils. This tension between the district and the county councils was to play no little part in the eventual outcome.

Other responses were also negative, with or without qualification. The AWA and the Port and Haven Commissioners were opposed, as were the boat-hiring and, above all, the farming interests. The latter saw a National Park simply as detrimental to agriculture and food production. Others, while seeing no need for a National Park, were in favour of some form of central authority. These included the tourist, sport and recreation organizations, the Standing Committee on the National Parks and all the local conservation societies. The NCC produced a detailed paper which was described by the commission as "a most persuasive assessment of the significance of the area for wildlife", but saw no need for more than better co-operation and a willingness to take effective action, perhaps guided by a "Broads Officer". Among individuals there was a significant divide, those outside the area being generally in favour of designation while local residents expressed more varied views. Almost the only body unequivocally in favour was the National Trust.

Having received these responses, the commission issued a second document in the summer of 1977. This contained a summary of the views that had been expressed, together with an outline of four possible courses of action. In essence, these options were:

A. Designation as a National Park under existing legislation.
B. Designation, but with additional legislative powers over water quality and navigation.
C. Establishment of a special authority.
D. The Anglian Water Authority to be given navigation powers.

The commission spelt out in some detail the implications of each of these options. It stressed that A and B would have the advantages of creating a unified responsibility for planning and development control, together with a system of management guided by a plan that would enable the Broads to be used "more closely to their capacity". National involvement and Exchequer finance would be attracted. The planning functions of the district councils would become those of the Park Committee, but two-thirds of the latter's membership would be in local hands. Option A could be implemented under existing powers, but option B would require amending legislation although it might produce an authority better equipped to cope with the special problems of the Broads. Option C was very similar to the proposals put forward by the County Planning Officer in 1971 and would also require legislation. Provided there was enough local support for it, it had the advantage of flexibility and variants could be considered to accord with local wishes. Option D would provide for a single authority to control all aspects of river management.

The commission then outlined its own preference. This was for option B, which it saw as providing an authority with all the functions and resources which were needed in the special conditions of Broadland. Finally the commission sought to dispel what it saw as some misconceptions that the responses had revealed about the National Parks system. It stressed that a Broads National Park would not entail any large public ownership of land, nor—a crucial concession—would it include a large area of agricultural land. In the words of John Cripps, chairman of the commission, it did "not expect the boundaries to cut deep into the country, but to 'keep closely to the edge of the broads". Tourist publicity would "not be greatly increased"; the commission agreed that the Broads could not absorb unlimited numbers of visitors. The area would still be administered by local authorities and the interests of local people would not be ignored. There would be improved managerial arrangements and less *ad hoc* consultation. The National Park type of management plan was important.

A further round of consultations then ensued, based on this more structured view of what might or might not be possible. At its conclusion, the commission issued a further document summarizing the outcome and setting out the conclusions it had reached. This revealed, on the one hand, that there was practically no local support for a National Park in the existing form, nor, at the other extreme, was there any enthusiasm for a mere transfer of navigation powers to the water authority. Both were seen as inadequate solutions for the particular problems of the Broads. Option B was suported by a large number of conservation and amenity societies, and it was a second choice for some other groups. Some of them suggested that the problems of control over water and navigation could be met by giving the authority some form of statutory control of standards and over boats, to which the responsible bodies would have to conform (a solution which, as far as water is concerned, has now been applied nationwide with the formation of the National Rivers Authority). Others suggested that the water authority should be statutorily required to operate "in general accord with" a National Park plan, and that there should be a licensing system to control the number of boats. It also emerged that there was much support among the conservation and amenity societies, including the NCC, for the proposition that the boundary of the National Park should be drawn widely, to include large areas of surrounding farmland (as a buffer zone and to control undesirable land changes) and villages (to control development). On the option as a whole, the commission commented that it would be likely to be opposed by the local councils and the statutory agencies in the area on the grounds that it would strengthen National Park powers at their expense and, for the same reason, might not be acceptable to the government. There was also some support for option C but at the same time very little precision about how a special authority might be constituted and operated. The commission concluded that it was very unlikely that the government would agree to finance such a body and transfer to it the powers of the existing statutory agencies.

If the Countryside Commission had thought that by putting up a few Aunt Sallys, it would be able to convince local opinion that its preferred solution of a modified National Park was the only reasonable one (even though it had had to concede that it would not be witout problems), it was destined to be sadly mistaken. Its disappointment was shown by some tart comments in its report, not least to the effect that the debate on its consultation paper had largely ignored the considerations that the Broads were of national importance as a landscape and recreation resource, and that designation as a National Park could bring into play "a range of powerful measures" to improve the management of the Broads' natural resources. For what had emerged during the debate—and had not been sufficiently appreciated by the commission—was the strength of opposition to an "outside solution" which would both dilute and alter the balance of local statutory powers. The commission had not exactly endeared itself to local opinion and it is not surprising that given its record nationwide the National Parks model did not appeal. Apart from this, there was no little prejudice against an authority which would have a large measure of outside representation and which would, it was thought, introduce an added burden of bureaucracy and expense.

The local authorities not only expressed their scepticism about the Countryside Commission's various formulations, but took the initiative in proposing a solution of their own. This came from the Norfolk branch of the Association of District Councils, reflecting the anxiety of the district councils that they should retain more of a presence in the planning and decision-making process than would be the case if any of the commission's options for a new authority were to be implemented. No new authority, it was argued, was necessary since the local bodies already had the powers to cope with the situation. The real need was for better co-ordination. This could be achieved by reconstituting the Broads Consortium as a joint executive committee of the local authorities, to be known as the Broads Authority. This would have delegated powers and would consist of a Broads Officer with a small administrative staff and some local financing.

By the time that the Countryside Commission came to pronounce on the second round of consultation, a working party of officials had already put flesh on this proposal and Norfolk County Council had gone on record formally (by a vote of thirty to twenty-three, across party lines) as preferring it to any of the commission's options. Having been thoroughly out-manoeuvred, therefore, the commission had very little choice other than to accept it. It could—and did—point out that the previous consortium had proved unable to stop the progressive decline of the Broads, but it had to concede that more powers would be given to the new authority and that it was clearly supported by a good deal of political will. It also had to admit that it appeared to be by far the quickest solution and that the proposed level of local financial investment was "comparable to the highest levels for individual existing national parks". Looking over its shoulder, it must also have realized that governmental support for any solution which needed legislation would be problematic in the face of a locally favoured alternative. It had also itself conceded that some form of local arrangement would be necessary for the interim period until legislation had been passed. For all these reasons, therefore, the commission announced in April, 1978, that while it still took the view that the Broads were of sufficient character and significance to merit designation as a National Park, it would defer a decision on this in the light of the local initiative. If by the end of 1978 satisfactory progress in setting up the authority had not been made, or if by the end of 1980 the authority had not itself made satisfactory progress, then National Park designation would be proceeded with. Designation would in any case be reconsidered in 1983. In the meantime the commission would support the authority with grant aid and advice. It would also expect the authority to consult it about the boundary of the Broads, to produce a management plan and an annual report, to agree with it the appointment and job description of the Broads Officer and to accept three commission representatives as members of the authority.

The Broads Authority thus came into existence less on its own merits than as the expression of a local determination not to surrender more power to outside interests than was absolutely inescapable. Visitors, if not unreservedly welcome, at least contributed a good deal of income to Broadland enterprises, but the corollary that there was a case for a substantial national presence when it came to running the Broads was by no means as acceptable. Of the twenty-six members who attended the first formal meeting of the authority in September, 1978, five were appointed by Norfolk County Council, two by Suffolk County Council and two each by the six relevant district councils. Of the remainder, two were apppointed by the AWA, two by the Port and Haven Commissioners, and the final three by the Countryside Commission. Thus not only was the proportion of local authority representatives appreciably higher than in a standard National Park committee, but the normal numerical predominance of county council over district council representatives was more or less reversed. In local as well as in national terms, therefore, the grass-roots principle prevailed.

The legislative cover for the authority was contained in Sections 101 and 102 of the Local Government Act 1972, which enabled local councils to delegate powers, in this instance those for planning and recreation. A legal agreement was drawn up between the local authorities and the authority, formally defining the authority's objectives in the following terms:

> Recognising the national importance of the area for its landscape, nature conservation and recreational value the overriding consideration is:
> 1. To conserve and enhance the natural beauty and amenity of the area as a whole including its wildlife, while
> 2. protecting the economic and social interests of those who live and work in the area and preserving its natural resources, and
> 3. facilitating the use of the Broads for recreational and holiday purposes both waterborne and land-based and for the pursuit of scientific research, education and nature study.

This clear statement of the overriding importance of the conservation of natural beauty and wildlife is significant in the light of what was to happen a few years later.

Upton Broad. One of the "hidden places", and one of the few broads still in an unpolluted state, although a danger of pollution from neighbouring farmland recently emerged.
P. A. Ewans

The relationship between the authority on the one hand and the AWA and the Port and Haven Commissioners on the other was less easy to define, since neither could legally delegate any powers. Any joint action would have to be the product of co-operation and diplomacy, through the good offices of those bodies' representatives on the authority. Among the immediate problems which had to be resolved were those of determining the boundaries of the Broads area and the appointment of the Broads Officer. In the case of the boundary, the local councils had no hesitation in drawing it as tightly as possible, to the extent that the total area covered only 108 square miles, well under two-thirds of the area suggested by the Hobhouse Committee and the Broads Consortium. Only in following the valley of the Bure as far as Aylsham did the boundary exceed the earlier projections, while in general it followed closely the limits of the flood plains, rigorously excluding any portion of the valley slopes or uplands. The coastline was also totally excluded, as was much of the marshland in the Hickling/Horsey basin.

Less straightforward was the task of finding a Broads Officer—not on account of any shortage of candidates, since the authority had some 1,500 applicants from which to choose, but because the first two selected turned down the job once they had taken a close look at it. Part of the problem was that the post did not fall into the natural career structure of a local government officer. More critical considerations were well put by a correspondent in the *Eastern Daily Press*:

> The job that the hapless man would be expected to do is an impossible one. He must somehow change everything for the better; somehow reconcile the conflicting claims of naturalists, hire fleets, navigation, farmers and sportsmen; somehow harmonise the jarring voices of a dozen or so local authorities. And he must do all this without offending anyone and without any clear brief as to what his priorities should be.

It was not until the summer of 1979, after a further five hundred applications had been processed, that Dr Aitken Clark was chosen for the post. This turned out to be an inspired choice, since Dr Clarke's qualifications combined a distinguished academic background—and hence an understanding of the importance and handling of research—with personal experience of local government.

The authority then began to take the measure of the various problems awaiting it. But it was not very far down the road when it encountered a situation which none but its worst enemies would have chosen for it: a head-on confrontation with its farming community which, on account of national implications, rapidly involved the heavy artillery of the National Farmers' Union and the Country Landowners' Association.

The Halvergate   13
Controversy: Phase
One (1980–1982)

The landscape is going to change whether we like it or not. The
Broads Authority can't dictate to the farmers what they are going to
do on the marshes.

A speaker during a Broads Authority meeting

The heartland of the Broads grazing marshes lies in the Halvergate
triangle, that stretch of land some 7,500 acres in extent bounded by
the Bure to the north and by Breydon Water and the Yare to the
south, and to the west by the rising ground lying between Acle and
Reedham. In winter these marshes are bleak and windswept, but
they are also areas of great beauty, where the traditional
agricultural practices have created and preserved an open landscape of soft and varied colouring, broken only by patches of
willow, scattered gateways and the gaunt towers of now derelict
windpumps. As elsewhere in Broadland, the dykes across Halvergate are valuable for their aquatic flora and fauna, and they contain
many species which have been lost with the degradation of the
water quality in the main rivers and broads. In the past, the area
has been an exceptional habitat for wildfowl and waders, which
were crucially dependent on the traditional grazing regime with its
unimproved grassland and seasonal flooding. Several species of
raptors, including harriers and short-eared owls, have also traditionally been attracted to the area. At the turn of the century it
was possible to see from the banks of Breydon Water some twenty
to thirty windpumps turning on Halvergate and beyond. Five were
still working in the nineteen-twenties along the banks of the
Halvergate Fleet, the main drainage dyke which runs for some two
and a half miles across the marshes. Many of the windpumps had a
small homestead for the marshman who operated the pump, kept
the dykes clear and tended the herds of cattle and sheep. The Fleet
was secured by a "summer wall" and a "winter wall" with some
twenty to thirty yards of land between the two which was known as
The Rands. A smaller version of the Ouse Washes, this strip was

inundated during the winter months and formed an ideal feeding ground for large flocks of white-fronted and pinkfeet geese. Even as late as 1938 some three thousand white-fronts were to be seen over the marshes and the pinkfeet were equally numerous. Both as a part of our agricultural heritage and for its overall environmental quality, Halvergate has been described as one of the most precious landscapes in Britain.

To retain the essential character of these marshes, there is no alternative to their continuing to be grazed. Without this, there would soon be a deterioration to scrubland; and without the maintenance of the embankments and drainage systems there would be extensive flooding and a reversion to reed-beds and lagoons. The botanical quality of the dykes, as well as the lushness of the grazing, is dependent on a high water level. It is also essential that the margins should be trampled and grazed by cattle, so that the water surface stays out of shadow. Although there has for a long time been a limited amount of arable within the grazing marshes, their character began to change significantly only with the introduction of modern drainage pumps. In 1934 a diesel pump was installed at the mouth of the Fleet, and this and others were replaced after the Second World War by more powerful electric pumps. With more consistent and prolonged lowering of the water levels, the marshes became drier and thus susceptible to arable conversion on a larger and more productive scale. This conversion nevertheless remained modest until the early nineteen-sixties but increased in the nineteen-seventies as it bcame evident that under the EEC agricultural support system there were considerable profits to be made from arable farming.

On the other side of the coin, the traditional livestock farming on the marshes was rapidly becoming unprofitable. Whereas, for example, some five thousand fattened cattle were being sold in Acle market each autumn during the nineteen-sixties, only about a tenth of this number were coming to the market by the early nineteen-eighties. An estimate made by Professor Timothy O'Riordan at the time was that, assuming a continuance of substantial EEC price guarantees on arable crops, fatstock might well have disappeared from the Broads marshes within a decade. The conversion to arable might indeed have been quicker and more extensive but for the problems of access for farm equipment, the fragmented patterns of land ownership, the problem of securing general agreement for the lowering of the water table, the acidity of some of the soils and, particularly among many of the smaller graziers, a degree of commitment to the traditional ways. Nevertheless, over Broadland as a whole, some twelve thousand acres of reclaimed marshland, about a quarter of the total, had been converted to intensive arable use over the previous twenty-five

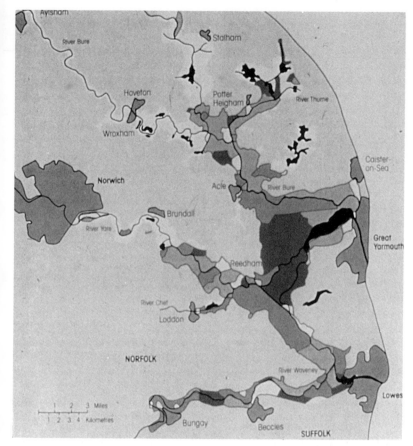

The destruction of the grazing marshes. This map shows the extent to which the Broadland grazing marshes had been degraded by the early '80s. The only substantial pristine area left was on the west side of Halvergate and south of Fritton Marshes.
Broads Authority

years, while in Halvergate the figure seems to have been about 2,200 acres. Nor was it just the conversion to arable that had been degrading the landscape; the process had brought with it concrete roads, new storage barns and overhead cables to power grain driers and drainage pumps, while fertilizers and pesticides had percolated into the dykes and damaged plants and wildlife.

It was not until the early nineteen-eighties, however, that the process became a matter of public concern. The trigger was the submission by the Lower Bure, Halvergate Fleet and Acle Marshes Internal Drainage Board late in 1980 of an application to the Ministry of Agriculture, ostensibly on behalf of some fifty Halvergate farmers. This was for grant aid towards the installation of four more powerful pumps, the deepening of some twelve and a half miles of drains and the construction of over three miles of concrete road, to facilitate a conversion to arable of some five thousand acres on the western side of the Halvergate Marshes. The drainage board was typical of the generality of these archaic bodies, which are responsible for the drainage of low-lying wetlands across the country. It could levy rates and attract Ministry of Agriculture grants for the maintenance and extension of drainage schemes, while being largely unaccountable, self-perpetuating and only minimally influenced by the smaller farmers among its membership, let alone by wider conservation or national interests. The scheme which it proposed on this occasion covered three areas in Halvergate, the Acle/Tunstall Level to the north-west, the Seven Mile/Berney Level to the south-west and the Manor House Level between them. The direct costs were estimated at some £1.26 million, to which individual farmers would add £1.1 million. The grant would cover half of the direct costs and about a third of the farmers' costs.

According to the drainage board's calculations, the investment would be justified by the increased profits from the change in land use; and the drainage board was also concerned that the existing pumps, which were thirty to forty years old, might fail at any time. While the latter argument was reasonable, the argument about profitability was quite the opposite since the economics were wholly distorted by public subsidies on both the conversion and the resultant crops. But the small clique of farmers who dominated the drainage board were of course concerned with the profitability to themselves, and the fact that the nation stood to make a net financial loss from the conversion was the last thing to enter into their calculations. It was estimated that a farmer with land on the marshes would have been able to multiply his annual profit roughly eight times by converting from beef cattle to winter wheat, while land values after drainage might have increased by a factor of 2 to 2½. All this would be with the benefit of public subsidies of some £1,600 per acre for the production of unwanted grain on that part of Halvergate that represented virtually the only coherent remaining area of environmentally significant grazing marsh.

This was not the first time that a Broadland internal drainage board had applied for a Ministry of Agriculture grant towards arable conversion. Only a short while earlier the Muck Fleet and South Flegg Internal Drainage Board had managed to obtain a grant towards the canalization of a section of the Muck Fleet Drain, just north of the Bure from Halvergate, with the result that several thousand acres of grazing marsh were converted to arable, penalizing many grazing farmers in the process. In the case of Halvergate, therefore, it was fortunate that the Ministry of Agriculture had recently initiated a policy of notifying local authorities of any applications for land drainage, otherwise that scheme too might have been quietly approved. As it was, the drainage board were asked to consult the Broads Authority and the

latter had the opportunity to object. The grant was withheld and negotiations began in an effort to reach a solution that both parties could accept. Broadly on the side of the authority were the Countryside Commission and the NCC, although with differing attitudes and concerns. The drainage board, on the other hand, which showed no appreciation at all of the environmental value of the area, was backed by the National Farmers' Union and the Country Landowners' Association, who were quick to see the implications of any agreements reached over Halvergate for the balance between farming and conservation interests nationwide. Indeed, as time went by, with an eye to the precedents to be set under the new Wildlife and Countryside Act of 1981, these two organizations virtually took over the running from the drainage board. But it was the local and national unofficial conservation bodies, the most militant among them being the Friends of the Earth and the most astute the Council for the Preservation of Rural England (CPRE), that ultimately played the most decisive role in the affair.

The Broads Authority started with a number of handicaps. It was relatively new and insecure, it had only just worked out a landscape policy, it contained many farmers among its members and, in general, it was reluctant to "make waves". Above all it had a major problem of finance, arising from the requirement that if the

Halvergate Marshes. The traditional grazing regime depends on the maintenance of a high water table. P. A. Ewans

ministry's grant were to be withheld permanently compensation would have to be paid and management agreements offered to the farmers concerned. The rates of compensation, moreover, would be bound to be high, since they would have to take into account not only the inherent value of the land but also the availability of conversion grants and the high EEC intervention prices for cereal crops. The costs might be as high as £200 per acre. Although the Countryside Commission would bear fifty per cent of the sum, it was still way beyond the financial capacity of the authority to conclude such agreements across the board. Another problem for the authority was that it was the government's policy not to grant aid replacement pumps on the grounds that they would not bring about any increase in productivity from the land in question. So the possibility of preserving the grazing while financing the necessary flood prevention measures was effectively ruled out.

It was therefore only with great difficulty and after some weeks of pressure from the Countryside Commission and various conservation bodies that the authority managed to string together a policy. At a meeting held early in 1981 a resolution was passed which described the proposed changes as unacceptable, called for a public inquiry if the ministry were to go ahead and fund them, and authorized a continuance of the negotiations which had begun with the drainage board. This resolution went against the advice of the authority's Strategy Committee and was opposed by a substantial minority of the authority itself, one of those present being reported as having made the assertion quoted at the head of this chapter. The decision to make a stand was thus only narrowly achieved and the formulation of a robust negotiating position was, at this stage at least, out of the question. The authority effectively set its face against arable conversion only in the case of some 1,100 acres near Berney Arms which it considered to be of the highest conservation value. For this area it proposed agreements that would be subject to arbitration and made it clear that any drainage proposals would be opposed. For the remainder it chose to rely on wholly voluntary agreements that the farmer could ignore if a figure for compensation could not be agreed. In all cases the farmers concerned would receive annual compensation payments over twenty years, in return for a commitment to continue grazing the land under conditions designed to preserve it in its traditional state.

The implications of these proposals were not lost on the conservation societies. Management agreements were widely seen as opening up possibilities of blackmail, which could be exercised without the farmer having any serious intention of ploughing the land. Nor did the conservationists accept the proposition that compensation should be paid for not implementing a scheme which would not have been contemplated but for public subsidies.

In a letter to *The Times* in August, 1981, the Director of the CPRE fired a major broadside. It was now much more likely, he argued, that other Broads wetlands would be drained: eighteen thousand acres of similar marshland were immediate candidates for comparable drainage, and compensation payments to safeguard the most valuable of them would, on the Halvergate model, cost the taxpayer £1 million a year (an estimate, incidentally, which was widely regarded as excessive at the time but which was borne out by later events). It was hardly conceivable that such sums would be on offer and the farmers would not settle for anything less. So the odds were that no future management agreements would be made and that could spell the end of the classic Broadland landscapes. Moreover, the economics of the scheme were dubious and had not been challenged. There was a clear alternative to such "open-ended guarantees to pay farmers for entirely hypothetical losses", namely to replace the pumps at their current capacity and so maintain the existing drainage regime and the grazing wetland. The whole issue should be the subject of a public inquiry. The Chairman of the Norfolk Society also weighed in. He asserted:

Mutton's Mill on Halvergate Marshes.
P. A. Ewans

> The mathematics seem crazy. We the taxpayers would pay to deep drain and irreversibly change the land in question. Second, we would pay compensation to some farmers for not taking advantage of the change. Third, we would pay the EEC intervention price for any resulting grain that was surplus to market requirements: and, fourth, we would pay for storing this surplus until we sold it off at a throw-away price to countries like Russia.

Strong doubts were also expressed about the role being played by the leaders of the drainage board.

The negotiations between the authority and the drainage board were long and convoluted. At one stage in the summer of 1981, after the Countryside Commission had broken ranks with the authority and pressed for a public inquiry, a deal was nearly reached. Compensation at the rate of £65,000 a year, or about £60 an acre, was proposed for the core area, with concessions being made in the shape of an offer by the farmers to withdraw their proposal for the Manor House Level (part of which consisted of an SSSI) and the authority its objections to the Acle/Tunstall scheme, where there was already a good deal of arable land. However the authority subsequently withdrew its offer and was persuaded to await the passage of the Wildlife and Countryside Act in the hope that this might enhance its negotiating position. Attitudes then began to harden. Taking account of the "blackmail" argument, the authority stipulated that compensation would be payable only for "proven loss of value", the farmers being required to show that the proposed improvements were needed, that there was a clear intention to carry them out, and that there was a financial and

141

technical capacity to do so. The farmers for their part were demanding index-linking of the compensation payments and management fees in addition to compensation, the scale of which they had pushed up beyond the estimates of independent assessors and, indeed, beyond the possibility of agreement. At one stage they even went so far as to sabotage much of the authority's efforts by removing a sluice on the Halvergate Fleet, which had the effect of draining the Manor House Level and lowering water levels in the core area itself.

In September, 1981, the authority proposed a "pause for reflection". By early 1982 they were considering a plan to buy out the farmers in the 1,100 acre core area and then sell back the land at a lower price under perpetual covenants preserving its traditional features. This might have cost £1 million at the outset, but would entail no ongoing compensation. It was not, however, agreed and by the spring of 1982 a total breakdown in negotiations seemed imminent. The passage of the Wildlife and Countryside Act had, if anything, made matters more difficult for the authority by enshrining the principle of compensation in its Article 39, while the drainage board showed a cavalier disregard for the obligations they now had under the Act to have regard to conservation and amenity aspects when proposing land drainage schemes. They also made matters even more difficult by refusing to allow a differential in land drainage rates which by alleviating the burden for the graziers would have made it easier for them to continue to farm in their traditional way. The situation was not improved when one Halvergate farmer quite legally ploughed twenty-two acres of an SSSI, not having been formally notified that he had land in this category. By September, 1982, after further exchanges, the authority had whittled down their proposals to the purchase and resale of a mere 440 acres. This would have entailed a one-off payment of £300,000 to just three landowners, the land being bought at £1,200 an acre and resold at about £600, the difference representing the compensation element. Although the deal did also include the dropping of the proposal for a pump and an access road on the Berney Marshes, this was the last straw for the Countryside Commission, who had been watching the successive retreats on the part of the authority with increasing dismay. The Commission refused to pay their share of the cost (by now raised to seventy-five per cent) and added their voice to the calls for a public inquiry, which had been multiplying in the continuing absence of a settlement. They were soon joined in this by the authority.

From the outset, the government had insisted that a solution had to be found locally and on a voluntary basis. There is little doubt that they were far from happy with the concerted call for an inquiry, given all the controversy and pressure that it would be bound to generate and the fact that it would be proof of the failure of a major element of their brand-new environmental legislation. There is reason to believe that their displeasure was conveyed to the two authorities in unmistakable terms. But their hand was effectively forced and they had to drop their insistence both on the unacceptability of replacement pumps and on the need for a local solution. In November, without any consultation with the parties concerned, ministers announced a decision under Section 48 of the Wildlife and Countryside Act that they would finance one new pump of higher capacity for the Acle/Tunstall Level; that a second pump for the Berney/Seven Mile Level would be no more than a replacement of identical capacity; and that they would not grant aid the 1,250 acres of the Manor House Level at all. This was the very first use of Section 48, which requires the Minister to further the interests of conservation in land drainage schemes; it was also the first occasion when grant aid for agriculture was refused on conservation grounds without a public inquiry; and it effectively conceded that the government could not evade responsibility in conservation issues of this kind. To those extents, therefore, it was something of an environmental landmark.

The decision did not, however, meet with much approval. Friends of the Earth and others promptly condemned it on the grounds that it would entail public expenditure of over £1 million for what was, at best, only a partial measure of protection for the marshes. They also argued that improvement of the drainage would benefit only the bigger farmers, and that the smaller ones, for many of whom grazing was a way of life, would be pushed out of business by higher drainage rates. It was also pointed out that the permission which had been given for a road to the new Seven Mile pump would open up some of the most valuable grazing land, hitherto wellnigh inaccessible, to arable conversion, whether or not it was drained. For the farmers, on the other hand, it was argued that it was an injustice that they were being compelled to look after a national heritage at a financial cost to themselves. The area was neither an SSSI nor a National Park, and they had assumed that they could improve their land and gain a reasonable return from it. Being now unable to do this, there was a risk that they would have to allow much of the land to go untended. Nobody, therefore, was satisfied, nor in practice did the decision prove sustainable. What had been hailed as "a victory for common sense" soon turned out to be no solution at all.

★ ★ ★

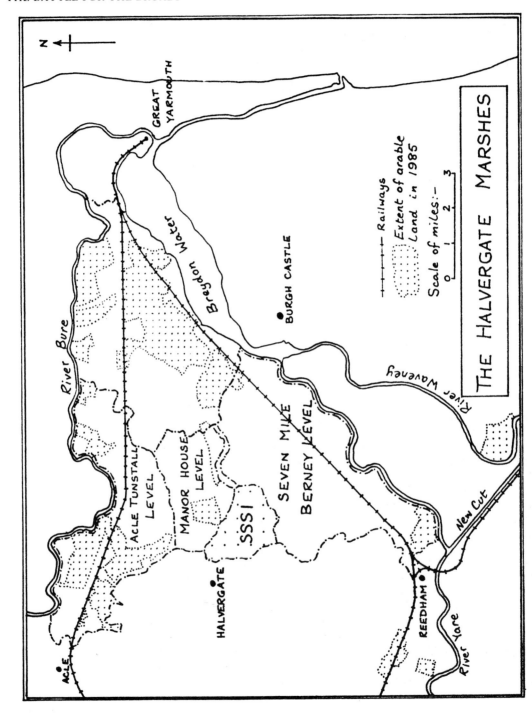

THE HALVERGATE MARSHES

The Halvergate Controversy: Phase Two (1983–1985)   14

Mr Jack Straw (Blackburn). Does the Secretary of State not already have power under Section 29 of the Wildlife and Countryside Act to make an order which extends to the whole area, including Halvergate Marshes, and does not the Minister of Agriculture have power to refuse to make discretionary grants for drainage, including the pumps? Why does not the Secretary of State use his powers under Section 29 to give a year's breathing space, as we have demanded?

Mr Jenkin. The short answer is that the Broads Authority, which is the planning authority for the area, has not asked me to do so. *[Interruption]*. It is all very well, but how often should Governments take matters out of the hands of those who are appointed to deal with them. *[Laughter]*. That is the truth of the matter.

Hansard

In 1983 the Broads Authority began to come under renewed pressure for arable conversion in the Halvergate area when five farmers notified it that they intended to convert 745 acres in the Seven Mile/Berney Level in the next growing season. The problem was not just that arable farming would be more profitable, but that the traditional grazing, both for beef fattening and for dairy farming, was becoming yet more marginal. Costs were rising across the board, while the dairy quota and declining grazing rentals posed additional complications. Even if the authority's share of the cost were to be no more than twenty-five per cent of the total, this would still amount to about a third of its total budget and was clearly too much for it to contemplate. According to the Broads Authority Chairman, this notification threatened to be only the beginning: he reckoned that some five thousand acres of grazing marsh would be at risk over the next five to seven years and that the authority would have to find well over £½ million per annum——perhaps as much as £1 million—in order to safeguard it. During the period 1980–83, conversion to arable had been proceeding at a rate of some eight hundred acres a year, and every indication was that the process would accelerate.

Long and difficult negotiations once more ensued, both with the farmers and between the authority, the Countryside Commission and the government. The authority now found itself with even less leverage over the farmers: the voluntary nature of Section 39 of the Wildlife and Countryside Act and the fact that grants for drainage were no longer part of the equation put the negotiating advantage square with the latter. Early in 1984 the Broads Agricultural Liaison Panel was set up as a conciliation forum, bringing together the Ministry of Agriculture, the conservation agencies and representatives of the farmers, but this made little impression on the problem. The authority was raised to the status of a *de facto* National Park under Section 41 (3) of the Act for the purpose of formalizing its eligibility for a seventy-five per cent grant for the funding of management agreements, but this was still far from sufficient for it to be able to contemplate undertaking any further responsibility for compensation. The authority pressed for ninety per cent funding on the precedent of Exmoor, but this was rejected by the government and, in any case, having to find even ten per cent would have been likely to overstretch the authority's resources. There was, however, now a belated recognition of the fact that if some solution could be found preventing a conversion to arable, the Ministry of Agriculture would be saved considerable expenditure on the resulting subsidies, by some calculations to the extent of some £100 per acre. Various proposals involving the ministry's assumption of financial responsibility were therefore discussed, including some form of capital grant or an increase in the funds made available to the authority from the government. Also considered were headage payments on the pattern established under the Less Favoured Areas (LFA) Directive, which provided for special measures of support, mainly for mountain or hill farmers. For one reason or another, however, all were rejected. In particular, the government were unwilling that the Broads should be treated as an LFA on the grounds that LFA subsidies should only apply to land that could not be made fully productive.

In this way, matters dragged on until well into 1984. Some of the farmers concerned were bought off temporarily by the offer of compensation at £20 per acre for one year; three of them accepted this. Two, however, the brothers Michael and David Wright, who between them owned some 375 acres on Halvergate, refused. To underline their refusal, they gave notice that they would start ploughing on 10th June, 1984. It was therefore less than wise for the Minister for the Environment, William Waldegrave, to announce in the House of Commons in April, 1984, that the Broads were "safe for a year". The effects of his doing so were to be highly embarrassing to the government as well as to himself personally.

Events moved fast in the course of May and June. Agreement was reached with Michael Wright towards the end of May, since it was felt that his land was of critical landscape importance. The authority was less concerned about David Wright's land, since although it was graded as top quality grazing marsh it was adjacent to land already converted to arable and hence reckoned to be less crucial from the conservation point of view. The authority was still worried about the cost of agreements, even if they covered only a single year, and—dare one say it—there may even have been the thought that a political storm would do no harm and that matters should be brought to a head. In any event, David Wright was refused an agreement and in effect given the go-ahead to plough. On 10th June, he started preparing to do so. The *Observer* carried the story on the same day and Friends of the Earth promptly demonstrated in front of the cameras and his dyke-digging machinery. Not liking the situation at all, he insisted that he was ready to settle. The authority, however, was unyielding, at least to the extent of not offering more than the standard holding payment, which he had already refused. Ploughing recommenced in the face of further protests by Friends of the Earth, and the political heat was on.

Meanwhile another farmer, in Limpenhoe, had also proposed to drain and plough some hundred acres of land, but had refused to negotiate any sort of management agreement. He intended to better his prospects, and that was that. In his case the CPRE came up with a new idea, that of constraining him from proceeding by a direction under Article 4 of the Town and Country Planning (General Development) Order, 1977, which would require him to obtain planning permission for any agricultural works he was proposing to undertake. He could plough, but he could not dig the necessary drainage. The Broads Authority asked the Minister of the Environment (with whom the responsibility lay) to apply the article and the *Observer* was again quick to report that the minister was having a problem in persuading his colleague at the Ministry of Agriculture to go along with it—the feelings of the farming lobby over such a breach of the voluntary principle, to which they attached overriding importance, can be readily surmised. It is said that the decision to apply the article was insisted on by the Prime Minister. However it came about, it was applied speedily and had the effect of persuading that farmer also to accept a one-year holding payment. The conservation lobby now had the bit between their teeth. There were demands that article 4 should also be applied to David Wright and, more generally, to any environmentally recalcitrant farmer or landowner within the grazing marshes. Patrick Jenkin, Secretary of State for the Environment, was given a bad mauling in Parliament, and uproar ensued when he tried to shelter behind the Broads Authority and to insist that it was for them, rather than him, to deal with the Wright affair, at least in the first instance.

The political compulsions thenceforth worked inexorably towards a comprehensive solution of the problem of the grazing marshes. During the rest of 1984 feelings ran high. Friends of the Earth and others swapped arguments in the press with the farmers and their representatives; ministers paid visits of inspection and were met by demonstrators; and Friends of the Earth tramped over the marshes, reporting any signs of an intention to plough. In a more general context, two House of Lords select committees, on the European communities and on science and technology, took major issue with the government's failure to co-ordinate their agricultural and environmental policies. Nor did the financial compulsions in any way diminish. In total, during 1984 and 1985 the authority had to conclude holding agreements on some 1,300 acres of land in the Halvergate area alone, while further notifications suggested that the total might soon rise to substantially more than that. The limits to the authority's ability to cope with demands of this magnitude were clear. Against this background, intensive behind-the-scenes consultations took place between the responsible ministries and organizations in an effort to come up with a solution.

In the spring of 1985, after nearly five years of manoeuvre, argument and negotiation between the government, the Broads Authority and the farmers, a solution was, at the instigation of the Countryside Commission, at last found. Under Section 40 of the Wildlife and Countryside Act, it was open to the commission to promote experimental schemes of countryside management for conservation purposes. By using a somewhat elastic interpretation of this rather imprecise section, cover was found to put in place a three-year Broads Grazing Marshes Conservation Scheme, funded equally by the Ministry of Agriculture and the Countryside Commission to the tune of £50 per acre per annum, cash-limited to £1.7 million in total. The idea was a highly innovative one in that it proposed a flat rate of subsidy across a whole environmentally valuable area, rather than individual management agreements negotiated as the need arose on a "profits foregone" basis. During the first year it covered most of the central Broads grazing marshes, but the area was extended during 1986 and 1987 to include marshes around the Bure to the north and the Waveney to the south. To strengthen the safeguards, the Broads were designated under Section 41(3) of the Wildlife and Countryside Act, which required farmers seeking ministry improvement grants to notify the Broads Authority of the changes they were proposing to make, whereas notification had up to that time been purely voluntary. Under the scheme, which was applicable to all Grade I and Grade II marshes, whether or not there was any threat of arable conversion, stocking levels were closely controlled, as was cutting for hay or silage; and a number of activities—such as the construction of buildings or roads, the improvement of the grazing, the removal of landscape features and the application of fertilizer or herbicides other than within strict limits—could be undertaken only with prior approval. The formulation of acceptable guidelines was no simple business, if only because it was found that at least eighteen different types of grazing system were practised in the marshes. Nevertheless, those concerned managed to have the scheme ready for the beginning of the 1985 grazing season, and Lord Belstead, the Minister of State for Agriculture, and Sir Derek Barber, the Chairman of the Countryside Commission, launched it at a press conference in Norwich on 16th March of that year.

At least as an interim measure, the scheme can be reckoned to have been a considerable success. The take-up was extensive, and by 1986 some 15,400 acres, varying between 92.5% and 95% of the total eligible, were covered by it. During the three years of its existence, the traditional grazing was largely preserved and the amount of land lost to arable was negligible, although its third objective, the reconversion of arable to grazing, was only minimally achieved. It was the first time that the Ministry of Agriculture contributed substantial funds to a conservation project, and the whole arrangement at last demonstrated that land management could be organized in the Broads in such a way as to support both farming and conservation. There is also no doubt that a good deal of land would have been lost to arable had the scheme not been in existence. A survey of the scheme published in 1988 suggested that the land identified as being at risk in 1984 might have been steadily converted to arable over a period of four years, at a rate representing an annual loss of the order of between 2½% and 4½% per annum of the total. The Broads Authority themselves reckon that but for the scheme a large-scale exodus out of grazing would have taken place, to the extent, perhaps, of more than three thousand acres. The financial calculations produced in the survey showed that over the period of the scheme, wheat growing remained significantly more profitable than most forms of grazing, even after taking the compensation into account.

Other interesting insights were provided by the survey. One was that there were inequities in the effects of the compensation on the incomes of the various types of grazing enterprise within the scheme, most landlords, for example, benefiting to a greater extent than owner-occupiers or graziers. Nevertheless the survey showed that the scheme had won wide local approval and that there was only limited support for any major changes to it. The authors of the survey rightly judged that after all the intensity of feeling and differences of view which had preceded the scheme, this was a noteworthy achievement. Nevertheless the survey concluded that, assuming the 2½%–4½% rate of threatened conversion a year, selective management agreements or the public purchase of land threatened with conversion would have been more cost-effective than the scheme, when taking into account both direct budgetary costs and also the savings on agricultural support costs. Indeed management agreements might have been fully self-financing in terms of net budgetary costs alone. The survey also suggested that the financial attractiveness of arable conversion had been declining since the inception of the scheme and that the scale of compensation agreed might with the benefit of hindsight have proved to be too generous. Indeed, the success of the scheme in terms of its high uptake might have been in some measure due to the farmers' anticipation of such a decline. However, against all this, the survey conceded that the scheme had had to be put in place hurriedly and in an atmosphere of intense political controversy. There had been no time for detailed study of the options, which had in any case been limited by political and financial constraints.

From the outset, the scheme was seen to be only an interim measure; indeed, even before it was put in place, the government announced that they were going to try to work out some more durable arrangement with a wider applicaton. The Halvergate affair was the immediate incentive, but the critical House of Lords reports mentioned above, together with the ensuing parliamentary debates, also had a major effect. The government's proposal was that they should approach the European Commission for a mechanism which would enable them to fund farmers "in suitably designated areas of high conservation value in order to encourage farming practices beneficial to the environment". The mechanism chosen was an amendment to the European Commission's Structures Regulation, its basic directive dealing with grant aid for agriculture. The idea was at first received with a certain amount of cynicism and ministers themselves seem to have had some doubts about the chances of its acceptability to the European Commission. But some hard bargaining in Brussels secured agreement for the amendment later in 1984, although with the stipulation that the finance should come from member governments. The criteria, to which the Broads grazing marshes neatly conformed, were that the areas should be of national environmental importance, that they should be discrete and coherent, and that their value should depend on the maintenance of particular farming practices, detrimental changes to which were threatened. So emerged the Environmentally Sensitive Areas (ESA) Scheme, and the Broads were designated an ESA in July, 1986. Across the Broads, the scheme lasts for five years from 1987, but the ESA designation is indefinite. Two tiers of compensation are in operation, set at £50 and £80 per acre per annum, the latter rate applying if the farmers implement extra conservation measures such as using less fertilizer and retaining a higher level of water in the dykes. The farmers covered by the Broads Grazing Marshes Conservation Scheme were transferred into the ESA Scheme in 1988. The option of including management agreements is still open, but their greater expense is causing the Broads Authority to keep them in reserve for situations in which something more rigorous is needed than the normal mechanism.

The Broads Grazing Marshes Conservation Scheme and the controversy leading up to it are now a matter of history. Along with Exmoor and the Somerset Levels, Halvergate has gone down as a *cause célèbre* in conservation folklore. Although widely—and correctly—seen as a confrontation between farming and conservation interests, this is by no means the whole truth. It did indeed mark a major shift in influence from the farmers to the conservationists, but there were many former who were keen to continue to work

Looking across the Waveney from Burgh Castle to the Haddiscoe and Halvergate grazing marshes. Berney Arms Mill and Mutton's Mill on Fleet Dyke are silhouetted against the uplands of Wickhampton and Halvergate.
P. A. Ewans

their land in the traditional ways, and also many conservationists who wanted no more than that farmers should be able to do that. As happens not infrequently, extremists on both sides made a solution harder to attain than it need have been. A truer verdict would be that the traumas that arose were unlikely to avoided in the conditions of the time. The government's legislation, highly controversial in itself, was untested and, as it turned out, inadequate, and nobody had really applied their mind to the solution of conservation problems of this particular nature. It is sad that the price has been what Professor O'Riordan has called a "museumisation" of the now unviable type of agriculture being practised on the marshes, but there is clearly no alternative that would provide the protection needed. It is also a fact that in strict market terms arable farming would be equally unviable. At the end of the day, it is a cause for satisfaction that effective action was eventually stimulated in defence of a valuable piece of countryside that was undoubtedly under very serious threat. Even more satisfactory is the fact that the solutions arrived at, in particular the ESA Scheme, had a more general application. Nationwide, nineteen ESAs have been created in the past five years and a further twelve are in prospect over the next two, although in general the proportion of farmers participating has not been as high as in the Broads. The ESA scheme is also likely to be further extended and improved in the Broads themselves.

In very local terms, a particularly welcome aspect is that part of the funds made available were devoted to helping the RSPB purchase their reserve at Berney Arms, described earlier. The initial flooding of seventy acres of this reserve has had remarkable results. Seven hundred Bewick swans have been using the area as a roost, while flights of barnacle, white-fronted and bean geese have appeared, together with two thousand wigeon and significant numbers of snipe and other species of duck and waders. Avocets have tried to breed, although so far without success. The aim now is to attract more birds by raising water levels more generally, the farmers being attracted to this by the higher tier of payment for which they would then be eligible under the ESA arrangements. Perhaps the most revolutionary step of all after centuries of pumping water out of the marshes, a pump is being installed on the Fleet to transfer to the marshes some of the fresh spring water presently being lost.

★ ★ ★

The Approach to Legislation

15

Over the years, the Norfolk Society has seen a worsening situation, an inability on the part of the Broads Authority to handle the situation effectively and the Broads emerge as a near-uncontrolled mass recreational facility. The Bill, concerned as it is with the future and essential qualities that sustain the Broads, ensures that many and varied sectional interests must sit down at one table and compound effective co-ordinating policies, for their very survival is at stake.

It is accepted that there will be differences of opinion but, nevertheless, we cannot but deplore the continuing pressures of the boating interests . . . led by the Great Yarmouth Port and Haven Commissioners. Their unilateral pursuit of their sectional interest, in the teeth of all the evidence, is far from the central purpose of the Bill, the achievement of a constructive balance. If they persist, the inexorable decline of the past half-a-century will continue beyond the point of no return.

Up to the time when pollution of the Broads effectively began, the River Thames, flowing past the Palace of Westminster, was a foul, sewage-sodden ditch. Today, salmon swim in a cleansed and rehabilitated river and it is our beloved Broads that are sinking, sullied and manifestly unclean.

Harold Rose, Chairman, Norfolk Society

Distracted for all of five years by the Halvergate affair and hindered by initial staffing problems, the Broads Authority made a slow start in setting itself up and getting to grips with the backlog of problems with which the Broads were faced. When the Countryside Commission came, as scheduled, to review progress at the end of 1980, its generally encouraging comments were tempered by several criticisms. The commission expressed the view that the authority had established itself as a strong, independent voice in the Broads—"no mean task in the present uncertain economic climate". It had shown that it had the potential to improve the Broads environment and was the agency "best fitted to address the landscape, conservation and recreation management problems of the area". There was thus, at that stage, no case for National Park designation. The commission would continue to support the authority and give it grant aid, pending a final review of the

"Our Broads are manifestly unclean." This photograph accompanied the letter of protest published by the Chairman of the Norfolk Society in October 1985. Anglia Television

position at the end of 1983. The commission went on to suggest that the authority's experience would be of value to the government, to itself and to others if a review of the administration of "designated areas" were to be undertaken at a future date. The commission believed that the authority should be formally supported by the government and would approach the Minister of the Environment in that sense.

However, the commission was not so happy about the authority's actual achievements. It noted that work on the Strategy and Management Plan had started much later than intended, that the first annual report had not yet been published and that a very slow start had been made on a programme of small-scale environmental projects. The commission put this down to a shortage of staff and reminded the constituent councils of their undertakings to provide adequate staff from within their own resources.

The authority's obligations were thus clearly established. It had to produce somewhat more to show on the ground and it had to publish the comprehensive plan that had been required under its initial terms of reference. Wisely, however, it decided that it would not be rushed into action except on the basis of thorough investigation into what were often complicated and controversial problems. It set in train, under the guidance of the expert Broads Research Advisory Panel, a series of research and experimental projects concentrating mainly on the interrelated questions of water quality, the management of broads and dykes, bank erosion, and soil and vegetation surveys. It also set up three committees with widely drawn, expert membership to work out policies and advise it on the landscape, ecological and recreational aspects of its work. Towards the end of 1982 it eventually published its draft Management and Strategy Plan under the title, *What Future for Broadland?* This was a refreshing document, in that rather than just reviewing the problems it listed no fewer than ninety-one specific policies, with indications of targets and timescales as well as of resources needed and of the agencies who would have to be responsible for implementation. The authority started by pointing out that its terms of reference required it to give priority to the preservation and enhancement of the natural beauty and amenity of the Broads, and that policies with these objectives in view would involve a major proportion of its resources, both human and financial. Environmental management would include the conservation of existing habitats and features of wildlife, landscape and historic importance, with the improvement of water quality an important aspect of this on account of its influence on many of the area's environmental problems. Efforts would also be made to restore areas that had deteriorated environmentally or, if that were impossible, to encourage the formation of "new and interesting landscapes". So far as recreation was concerned, the authority would concentrate on measures to relieve congestion at heavily used locations—responsibility for water recreation facilities lay with the Great Yarmouth Port and Haven Commissioners.

Looking at its resources, the authority acknowledged the assistance it had received in terms of manpower from its constituent partners, but concluded that it would need more specialist staff of its own. Inevitably, as it increased its involvement in projects and research in areas in which it had not so far made any progress, and as the results of current research showed where projects of environmental improvement were needed, expenditure would be bound to increase. This would be to some extent offset by a decline in expenditure on recreation and information policies after the initial investments had been made. The authority went on to warn, however, that its financial calculations omitted several potentially major areas of expenditure, including management agreements to safeguard areas of marshland, the purchase of marsh or fen areas of environmental importance and projects for the restoration of broads. Although the authority had a reserve fund on which it could draw, increased finance would be required.

In effect, therefore—not to put too fine a point on it—what the authority was saying was that it foresaw that it was going to be prevented for financial reasons from carrying out the full programme of environmental improvements which it believed was needed for the Broads (its activities were, in fact, to be severely curtailed by financial restraints, the problem becoming particularly acute in 1984). Over and above this, it was evident from the list of policies that the authority had put forward for implementation that many of the most crucial and costly would be beyond its remit and would fall to other authorities to carry out. As far as the authority was concerned, therefore, a large proportion of its policy objectives were little more than expressions of pious hope. While it was true, for example, that the AWA had started a programme of phosphate stripping on an experimental basis at sewage works on the River Ant, the authority could only ask that the experiment should be continued. If the programme were to be extended to cover the whole River Bure catchment, the capital costs at 1981 prices would be of the order of £100,000 and annual recurring costs only a little less. Moreover, if phosphate stripping were to be extended to the Yare and the Waveney, the cost would be many times greater. That for the Whitlingham works on the Yare alone were estimated at well over £½ million. Effectively, therefore, the authority was wholly in the hands of the AWA for the solution of what was possibly the most crucial of all the Broads' environmental problems. All it could do as a statement of policy was to "ask the Anglian Water Authority to ensure that the general quality of effluents from sewage treatment works is maintained at a level which is adequate to protect the aquatic environment". Similarly, the authority was concerned that more environmentally acceptable dredging techniques should be introduced on the Broads, but were wholly dependent on the Port and Haven Commissioners for carrying out what might well be more expensive operations. Far too many of the authority's so-called policies were, due to the restricted nature of its powers and remit, in fact little more than exhortatory.

This, then, was the situation when the Countryside Commission once again started a process of consultation in the summer of 1983. It began from the position that the Broads remained of national importance for their landscape, wildlife and opportunities for recreation, and that they should be considered to be of equivalent status to a National Park. If only because the Broads Authority had achieved a good deal within the previous five years, a continuing need had been demonstrated for a managing and co-ordinating agency that would be no less effective. The commission had no desire to suggest change for change's sake. However, apart from its 1978 commitment to undertake a review, there was the consideration that its agreement covering the authority's financial support, together with the government's grant aid, was due to run out in 1984. The commission then reviewed the authority's record at some length and posed a series of questions. Was the authority's current "co-ordinator/catalyst" style adequate, or did it need additional powers? Were its financial and staffing arrangements appropriate? Was its project and research programme well targeted? Had it gained public support? Had it exercised its powers effectively? Had it influenced and received adequate co-operation from its partners? Had it received sufficient national support? Were its boundaries appropriate?

While taking care not to pre-empt the answers to these questions, the commission nevertheless contributed some pointers. It was not happy about staffing levels. It believed that the authority's responsibilities for planning and development control had worked well and in the national interest, but doubted whether it had adequate powers to tackle such problems as control of navigation, water quality, bank maintenance and agricultural change. As for its relations with other executive agencies, the commission concluded that the other agencies' attitudes had "not always helped in the achievement of the Broads Authority's objectives and [had] not fully recognised the national importance of the area".

The commission then went on to suggest a number of criteria by which a long-term arrangement for the Broads should be judged. It was vital that they should be generally recognized as being of national importance, which essentially required National

Park status. Any planning and management agency should have a number of members to represent the national interest, but it must also enjoy local support. It was also essential that it should have a stable and secure constitution with a sound basis in law, which would "not be too vulnerable to the activities of other agencies". It must have the right mix of powers to tackle the environmental problems of the Broads, together with secure and flexible funding, a significant proportion of which should come from national sources. It must be able to attract and retain suitable staff, and it must be able to build on the work already put in hand by the authority—"any proposed long-term arrangements for the area must not lose the momentum which has already been built up".

The commission set out three possible options: the continuance of the authority roughly on existing lines, the creation of a National Park authority, or the creation of a new statutory authority established under a private Act of Parliament. The commission was careful not to opt for any particular one, pointing out that all had advantages and disadvantages. The existing authority had proved itself and its continuance would attract widespread local support. It had a flexible constitution and could exercise most of the powers needed for environment protection. It could be argued that voluntary association was the best means of securing the co-operation of the statutory agencies. Continuity would also be assured. On the other hand, it would not enjoy the national status or political support of a National Park, nor the security of a status derived from statute and long-term government funding. The National Park option was the only fully satisfactory way of signalling the national importance of the area and would assure long-term funding, but this option would not build on the success of the authority, the representational balance between the county and district councils would be altered and there would be bound to be a delay, perhaps of several years, before a National Park authority could start its work. Legislation to remedy defects in the existing National Park model would raise issues of national policy and could be a long and difficult process which the commission did not feel it could justify. A special authority would get round many of these difficulties, but the preparation and passage of a private Act would also take a good deal of time and might raise problems of precedent. Funding might also be a problem. The commission concluded by inviting comments in advance of its final recommendations at the end of the year.

When, at the end of 1983, the commission had received a complete set of comments on the options it had presented, it was apparent that once again it had been pre-empted by the local authorities. Their calculations were not difficult to discern. First of all, they clearly remained determined to keep powers in their own hands as far as possible. For the district councils, this meant not surrendering them to a National Park committee that would be dominated by the county councils, and for all the local councils it meant not surrendering them to a National Park board that would enjoy an independent status and to which they would have to contribute a precept from their rates without being able to exercise a decisive control over its level or application. Consideration of the national interest was conspicuous by its absence from any of the responses given by the local authorities to the commission. At the same time, however, they clearly realized that it would be wise to try to attract a larger and more secure source of funding than the existing authority enjoyed, even if this meant conceding a greater measure of non-local presence and influence in any successor agency. The trick would be to ensure that the new agency would remain effectively under local control while attracting government funding at the National Parks level, that is at seventy-five per cent of total expenditure. As part of the bargain, Norfolk County Council conceded that it would not press for any significant change in the current balance of local authority representation. This enabled all the local authorities, supported both by the Association of District Councils and by its Norfolk branch, to present the commission with a united front sufficient to outweigh the dissenting voices, notably those of the AWA and the Port and Haven Commissioners. Both the dissenters strongly advocated the continuance of the existing authority and were firmly opposed to any dilution of their own powers. In a closely reasoned submission the NCC, on the other hand, came down on the side of the local councils, arguing that the environmental considerations required a new body with the power to manage navigation rights, influence water quality and grant-aid appropriate projects. Most commercial interests favoured a continuance of the status quo, but the National Farmers' Union, surprisingly, came out in favour of a new statutory authority, as did the Broads Authority itself. Virtually clinching the issue, the local authorities, led by Norfolk County Council, expressed themselves ready to promote the local Act of Parliament they saw to be necessary.

Faced, if not with a consensus, then with a substantial weight of opinion in favour of a new, statutory authority, the commission must have known that it would receive no governmental support if it tried to persist with the National Park option. It therefore accepted the inevitable with a minimum of argument and in its full report, issued in March, 1984, bent its energies to an analysis of how best a new authority might be brought into being and constituted. It also took the opportunity to rehearse what it saw as currently deficient in the management of the Broads and to suggest improvements. It warned that the promotion of a Bill would be a lengthy process, likely to take at least four years even if it were unopposed. Widespread consultation would be necessary. The commission would wish the Bill either to tap into existing National Parks legislation or to provide equivalent powers. Permanence of status and funding should be assured, and national interests should be properly represented. A strong and independent authority should be created, able to exercise in its own right all the powers available to the existing authority. While it was a fundamentally bad principle to divide up the hydrological management of a river basin and responsibility for water quality should therefore be left with the AWA, a sustained programme of water quality improvement should be undertaken, funded by one authority or the other. The objective should be to restore the broads and rivers to a state conducive to the re-establishment of aquatic plant life within the next ten years. A statutory obligation should be laid on the AWA to conform to such a programme as well as to consult the Broads Authority on its own annual capital programme.

So far as navigation was concerned, the commission was critical of what it saw as a lack of close contact between the authority and the Port and Haven Commissioners and was sceptical of the value of trying merely to make improvements in consultation. It was, for example, surprising that the authority had not been consulted over the commissioners' future dredging programme. Many of the problems it had noted eight years earlier—bank erosion, congestion and conflicts of interests between users—were still prevalent. There seemed no likelihood of the "fundamental shift in orientation" that would be required of the commissioners if matters were to be improved. The purpose of the river system had changed over time, away from navigation and trade towards recreation and tourism. The problems of the area needed to be tackled in a comprehensive and co-ordinated way, and the management of the water space was integral to the proper protection and restoration of the whole Broads system. For all these reasons there would be substantial advantages in the transfer of navigation powers to the authority.

The remainder of the commission's recommendations were less contentious. It was writing in the middle of the Halvergate affair, and so its thoughts about the safeguarding of the grazing marshes were rapidly overtaken by events. It commended the existing arrangements for handling development control and planning matters, while noting that consultation on developments outside the authority's executive area but within its advisory area had been limited. Many Broadland villages just outside the executive area had acquired modern housing developments which were out of keeping with the Broadland scene. As for membership of the new authority, the commission advocated (vainly, as it turned out) a smaller committee, "aimed at generating a tight, corporate identity with a clear direction for executive action". But the proportion of members representing "national" interests should be increased. Funding should be on the standard National Parks seventy-five/twenty-five per cent ratio, with the local authorities maintaining the value of their contributions in real terms. The boundary of the authority's executive area was "generally right".

Having delivered itself of this advice, the Countryside Commission concluded by handing over the lead to Norfolk County Council, to whom it would fall to promote the required legislation. The commission undertook to continue to assist and to be the principal point of contact with the government, but saw it as the task of the county council and the other local authorities to undertake the necessary consultations while the legislation was being drafted. Having been given its cue, the county council took centre stage and proceeded with the drafting and consultations. It was not, however, to find this at all a straightforward task.

The first area of difficulty lay in the direction of the Port and Haven Commissioners, who, as the Countryside Commission had all too clearly foreseen, were totally opposed to any transfer of navigation powers. A steering group set up under the chairmanship of John Alston, the leader of Norfolk County Council, failed to reach agreement. The problem was exposed to public view at a press conference held in April, 1985, in order to initiate public discussion of the draft Bill. The position of the commissioners was simply that they had always had the responsibility for the navigation, they had all the necessary experience and expertise, and they saw no reason for change. They were prepared to offer a "partnership" to the Broads Authority, but a transfer of powers was out of the question. The county council went so far as to offer the commissioners an agency agreement giving them day-to-day management under the overall policy control of the authority, but it was equally unprepared to compromise on the issue of ultimate control. Despite a warning in September in a letter to *The Times*, signed by Sir Peter Scott and others, that the refusal by the commissioners to join the promoters of the Bill in delegating a share of their powers to the new authority might well put the entire Bill in jeopardy, no agreement could be reached. An intervention by William Waldegrave and meetings with Whitehall officials also proved fruitless, and it is possible that the Private Bill, had it been proceeded with, would have foundered on the issue. The commissioners were in fact to maintain their opposition to the transfer of responsibility for the Norwich Navigation (ie the navigation up the Yare and the Wensum between Yarmouth and

Norwich) right up to the concluding stages of the passage of the eventual legislation through Parliament.

The second problem emerged later in 1985, when the county council were advised by the responsible parliamentary authorities, the Examiners of Petitions for Private Bills, that the Bill failed to meet the criteria for a Private Bill. The trouble was that the Bill was in fact "hybrid"—ie it had a general public application as well as affecting private or local interests, while, as one commentator put it, it "bristled with Government money from top to bottom". It is curious that neither the Countryside Commission nor the county council (nor their advisers) appear to have foreseen this complication, which killed the Bill stone dead in its intended form. The only possible solutions were that a member of Parliament who had been successful in the annual ballot for Private Members' Bills should be persuaded to sponsor the Bill or that the government should take it over. The problem as far as the government were concerned was to fit the Bill into the parliamentary session which was on the point of starting. A vigorous lobbying campaign was launched. This was successful in persuading the government to adopt the Bill, but not before the 1986–87 session. In this way a whole year was lost.

From the air, east of Norwich. This photograph gives an impression of the intensive farming which takes place in much of the immediate catchment area of the Broads. In the centre of the picture is Wroxham Broad and the neighbouring Bure broads. Ranworth Broad is at the upper right of the picture and Barton Broad at the upper left. Hickling Broad and Horsey Mere are in the centre distance.
Norfolk Library Services

The Broads Bill   16

The Bill recognises the Broads' national importance and special needs. It gives them a status equivalent to that of a national park, but with wider powers. It reflects and respects the interests of boat users and commercial shippers . . . and balances those interests with the overriding need to maintain and conserve for ever the Norfolk Broads for the enjoyment not only of boat owners, but others, such as anglers and bird watchers, who want to continue to enjoy the area and to conserve and maintain its distinctive and unique character. We believe that the combination of powers, duties and a firm financial base for the new Authority provided in our Bill should provide the means whereby the future of the Broads can be secured for ever.

William Waldegrave, Minister for the Environment

Having taken the decision to replace the abortive Private Bill, the government proceeded to draft their own version. While this was a much more succinct document, it kept to the essential purposes of the Private Bill, namely to re-establish the Broads Authority within a proper statutory framework and to give it powers to manage the Broads for conservation, recreation and navigation purposes. These objectives were set out in the pivotal passages of the Bill, which defined the authority's duties and functions, requiring it

to manage the Broads for the purposes of—
(a) navigation
(b) conserving and enhancing the natural beauty of the Broads;
(c) promoting the enjoyment of the Broads by the public.

and

to have regard to—
(a) the national importance of the Broads as an area of natural beauty and one which affords opportunities for open-air recreation;
(b) the desirability of protecting the natural resources of the Broads from damage; and
(c) the needs of agriculture and forestry and the economic and social interests of those who live and work in the Broads.

The Bill also spelt out the composition of the authority; provided for it to be the sole planning authority for the Broads, the boundaries of which were defined; and required it to produce a "Broads Plan" at least every five years, together with a map showing any areas within the Broads "whose natural beauty it was particularly important to preserve". The Bill gave the authority powers analogous to those accorded to local planning authorities in the National Parks, to regulate operations which might adversely affect the character or appearance of areas of "grazing marsh, fen marsh, reed beds or broad-leaved woodland", and to make by-laws to prevent damage to, and protect the public enjoyment of, land owned by the authority or in common use. A major section of the Bill specified the powers and functions of the authority over navigation, to be exercised through a "Navigation Committee".

Many of the provisions of the Bill were bound to be controversial, and indeed several were disputed at length and with vigour during the proceedings in Parliament. It emerged that there was a good deal of discontent on all sides over what was seen as a lack of consultation both on the original Norfolk County Council's Bill and on the government's successor to it. In the course of the Bill's passage, government spokesmen made it clear that their purpose had, first of all, been as far as possible to give the Broads the status of a National Park. As one of them put it,

> although the National Park model is not entirely apt for the Broads area because of the dominance of the water spaces, in a lot of respects the National Parks model is the correct one to build on, and in preparing the general public legislation the Government has wanted, as far as possible, to fit the Broads Authority into existing legislation where it is appropriate and give it duties and obligations placed on National Parks, to put it in the planning legislation in an appropriate place to give it planning and byelaw powers which are largely akin to those given to National Park authorities.

Although the government's use of existing legislation was clearly to some degree sensible and their desire not to break new ground understandable, particularly in the context of local disagreements over the content of the legislation, nevertheless much argument ensued about the appropriateness of the National Park model. Another controversial point on which the government insisted was that they were concerned to insert additional safe-guards for boating and shipping interests and to accord them stronger representation on the proposed authority, given that these lobbies had been totally opposed to the navigational provisions of the former Private Bill. The whole question of the composition of the Broads Authority was the subject of a good deal of argument, as was the absolutely central issue of whether the three main objectives of the Bill—conservation, recreation and navigation—should, as the government proposed, be accorded equal importance; or whether, as was maintained by many parliamentarians and all the private conservation bodies con-cerned, overriding priority should be accorded to conservation.

The manner in which Parliament dealt with the Bill and with these issues is highly instructive, showing on the one hand the thoroughness with which all points of view were aired and considered, but on the other the ease with which the government ensured that their points of view prevailed. At the end of the day, nobody could say that they had not had a fair chance to argue their case (or at least to argue the case for their being allowed to argue their case), yet the outcome was if anything more unfavourable to conservation interests than it had been at the outset. The major problem underlying all attempts to amend the Bill in any significant way lay in its "hybridity". This term relates to the fact that it was a Public Bill with some characteristics of a Private Bill—its provisions were specialized and localized and therefore did not deal equally and across the board with particular classes of people. To take one example, it obviously did not affect the British landowning and farming community as a whole, only those whose properties lay in the Broads area. Under established parliamentary rules, the government were obliged to give formal notice of their intentions so that those affected could consider their position. Thereafter the Bill had to go before Lords and Commons select committees so that any who felt that their interests had been unfairly prejudiced could petition for redress. The Catch 22, however, was that both in the select committees and in the other stages of the Bill's progress through Parliament, any amendment that might alter the balance of interests in such a way as to be likely to cause damage to those of a third party would lead to "re-hybridization". The third party would in turn have to be given the opportunity to petition, which would mean that the whole parliamentary process would have to start afresh. Government spokesmen were both quick and emphatic to point out that the entire Bill would then be lost; that it would be exceedingly difficult to find parliamentary time for its reintroduction; and that at best there would be likely to be considerable delay before it could again be inserted into the parliamentary timetable. There was also the problem that once the Bill had received its Second Reading in the Commons, its principles would be deemed to have been established and it would not be open to a select committee to do anything that might call them into question.

The Bill was presented in the House of Commons on 18th November, 1986, and received its Second Reading—the debate in which the general issues surrounding it were aired—over a period of some four hours during the evening of 1st December. As is not unusual with business of limited general concern, it was a lack-lustre occasion attended by only a small number of MPs, mainly those with East Anglian constituencies or with an interest in environmental affairs. Since the opposition parties were in agreement with the main thrust of the Bill, little or no heat was engendered and no divisions were called, although several MPs succeeded at least in pinpointing some of the Bill's more obvious areas of controversy.

At the outset, the government made clear their stand on the question of overall priorities. Introducing the Bill, the Minister for the Environment, Countryside and Local Government, at that time William Waldegrave, insisted that the Bill established a "vital balance" between the three objectives of conservation, recreation and navigation, which were "in their own way, equally important". It was around this contention that the main battle lines were drawn. Led by David Clark for the Labour Party and by Nigel Spearing, the Conservative MP for Newham South—who was tireless throughout the proceedings in the Commons in trying to ensure priority for conservation—MPs insisted that this aspect had to be given explicit predominance if the essential character of the Broads were to be restored and maintained, and if their continuing fitness for recreational and other activities were to be ensured. Representatives of conservation bodies argued the same point at length before the select committees, but possibly it was registered most effectively in the Second Reading in the House of Lords. There, Lord Melchett pointed out that the Bill was introduced

> because of widespread and longstanding concern about the deterioration in the conservation and amenity interests of the Norfolk Broads. It was not introduced because of concern about navigation or concern for some other interest such as agriculture in that area. It was introduced because of concern at the appalling loss of wildlife and loss of the natural beauty of the area.

And as Lord Hunt also expressed it,

> there is now . . . a conflict of interest between, on the one hand, environmental conservation and the protection of wildlife and nature, and, on the other hand, the enjoyment of the Broads by the public; developed, exploited and exemplified by tourism and leading to the proliferation of water sports . . . Conflicts will arise; conflicts have already risen. Whenever that happens in future, there must be an established priority which will prevail.

Before the House of Commons Select Committee, the conservation societies tried to achieve the inclusion in Clause 2 of a form of words giving the duty of conservation an overriding priority. They put forward similar arguments and maintained that the primacy of conservation had been accepted by ministers not only in the context of the present Bill (quoting Mr Waldegrave's declaration on the Second Reading, reproduced at the head of this chapter), but also in the case of the National Parks generally. On the latter point, the committee were reminded that in 1974 the then government had explicitly endorsed the "Sandford Principle", the recommendation by the Sandford National Parks Policy Review Committee that in cases where there was irreconcilable conflict between the two purposes of National Parks—namely the public enjoyment of the parks and the conservation of their natural beauty—priority should be given to the latter. It was also pointed out that the guidelines for the existing Broads Authority gave primacy to conservation.

Against all these arguments the government insisted on the necessity of a balance and warned of the danger of re-hybridization. With the same consideration in mind, the Commons Select Committee did not even require the government to enter a reply to the case on Clause 2 put forward by the conservation bodies, a decision which provoked accusations by disappointed conservationists that the committee had earlier taken a different view and had clearly been "got at". The government also pointed out that the local councils were united in opposing any imbalance in priorities and urged that the "consensus" over the Bill should not be upset, even though it was clear from the evidence given that no consensus in fact existed. There is also no doubt that the government could from the outset have given a decisive "conservation" lead had they been so minded. But this was far from being their purpose, and their warnings about the possible loss of the Bill were sufficient to enable them to carry the day.

The government thus conceded nothing of substance on the question of priorities. They did however try to improve their definition of the authority's duties by rewording the vital Clause 2. The House of Commons Select Committee then modified the rewording, so that, in its final form, Clause 2 (1) read:

to manage the Broads for the purposes of—
(a) conserving and enhancing the natural beauty of the Broads;
(b) promoting the enjoyment of the Broads by the public;
(c) protecting the interests of navigation.

They also introduced a new clause towards the end of the Bill: "References in this Act to conserving the natural beauty of an area include references to conserving its flora, fauna and geological and physiographical features."

The more precise wording on navigation was a response to representatives by navigational interests that the Bill did not adequately allow for the implementation of new navigational works where these might become necessary. The definition of "natural beauty" was intended to ensure that the term should cover species and features of conservational importance that might not be apparent to the eye and might therefore not be held to be included.

When the Bill came before the House of Lords Select Committee in December, 1987, the only significant item on the agenda was a renewed effort by the voluntary conservation societies to enshrine in it the primacy of the principle of conservation. This time they tried a different tack: their proposed amendment to Clause 2 retained the three responsibilities to be laid on the Broads Authority in the equally balanced form in which they had been approved by the House of Commons Select Committee, but qualified them by the addition of the words "in such a way as to ensure their long-term conservation". They pointed out that this wording reflected precisely the terms already used by ministers when introducing the Bill in both Houses of Parliament as well as the assurances given by the Prime Minister in a letter to the Council for the Preservation of Rural England:

> This authority will have the comprehensive powers to manage both the land and water areas which we believe are essential if we are to reverse the continuing deterioration in the ecology of the Broads. There is an urgent need to deal with the special problems of this wonderful landscape, which is of national importance both for nature conservation and recreation.

As well as rehearsing all the previous arguments, the conservation societies made the additional point that their amendment was based on the fundamental principles of the World Conservation Strategy, which it was important to write into domestic legislation. In response, buttressed by petitions against the proposed amendment which had been submitted by the local councils and the Port and Haven Commissioners, the government insisted that what was being proposed was no more than an attempt to introduce primacy for the principle of conservation "by the back door". If it were not to be regarded as a clear case of rehybridization, then at the very least its adoption would be very likely to provoke extensive litigation on the issue. The House of Lords Select Committee were not slow to take the point and turned the amendment down.

Given, therefore, the absence from the Bill of any clear mandate over priorities in the management of the Broads, a related aspect of it—namely the composition of the Broads Authority and the outlook and interests of its members—came to assume greater importance. In the Bill, the government proposed that the number of these members should be thirty-five. In reply to protestations that this number was excessive and would inevitably lead to an unwieldy, if not unmanageable, authority, they pointed out that the existing Broads Authority, which was without any navigational responsibilities, had twenty-six members and that the number proposed in Norfolk County Council's Private Bill was thirty-three. They went on to justify their calculation on the basis that, again in conformity with practice in the National Parks, there had first to be a clear majority of representatives of the local county and district councils. On the basis of four members from Norfolk

County Council and two from each of the other seven councils which between them covered the Broadlands area, this meant an initial eighteen places. It was also the practice in the National Parks that the Secretary of State should appoint half as many representatives as those of the local councils, and this accounted for another nine. Then—a departure from the National Parks precedent—there were a number of places which had to be found for bodies that in the government's view had to be represented: the Countryside Commission (two), the NCC (one), the Port and Haven Commissioners (two), the AWA (one) and the authority's own Navigation Committee (two). The grand total was thirty-five. The four navigation representatives were, the government contended, particularly important given that the Broads were in law a harbour and that the authority was going to have significant navigational responsibilities.

This calculation of course raised a number of questions and begged several others. In the first place, why not halve the whole number to nine from the local councils, three appointed by the Secretary of State and five others? This would create a much more manageable authority while still allowing all the stipulated bodies to be represented. On this, one can only infer that considerations of precedent and patronage were regarded as conclusive. The government were also insistent that the Broads were a national, not merely a local, heritage. This view was strongly supported in Parliament. Furthermore, apart from the navigation account, which would be funded from tolls, the government would be financing the authority to the extent of seventy-five per cent of its expenditure, with only twenty-five per cent (less the rate support grant element) coming from the local councils. So the argument for a majority of local council representatives was by no means self-evident, particularly as in the nature of things several of the remaining places would be bound to be filled by local people. However, yet again, the government were insistent that the standard National Park model had to be followed.

Perhaps even more glaring was the absence of any obligation to appoint a single member of any of the non-statutory conservation bodies with property and/or interests in the Broads area. These, as we have seen, had campaigned incessantly for a conservation-oriented Broads Authority and had themselves done a considerable amount over many years to preserve the Broadland heritage. It was all the more peculiar that such a key special interest should be ignored when the government had been careful to satisfy the navigation and boating interests to the extent not only of making provision for four representatives in the general list but also of adding the stipulation that the Secretary of State should appoint no fewer than three of his nine to represent boating

A yacht race on the Yare.

interests. Given also the existence of the special Navigation Committee, it is not surprising that the comment was made that this was going to be essentially a navigational authority with some conservation concerns added by the way. It was, moreover, proposed by the House of Commons Select Committee and accepted by the government that a further two of the Secretary of State's nine places should be filled by representatives of farming and landowning interests. The committee ignored all pressure for places for conservation interests, and the government were able to put the argument that five of the Secretary of State's places had already been allocated and it would not be right to restrict him further. The most that they were prepared to concede was that they accepted that in making his final four appointments the Secretary of State would have to "have regard to all other interests that may legitimately expect to be reflected in the membership of the Authority" and that it would be open to voluntary conservation and public amenity bodies to volunteer suggestions. The practical results of this calculation of the membership of the authority are discussed in the following chapter.

A separate area of controversy concerned the responsibility for navigation. The Port and Haven Commissioners maintained to the end their opposition to a transfer of their responsibilities for navigation, or at least for the Norwich Navigation. Michael Cartiss, the MP for Great Yarmouth, unsuccessfully introduced specific amendments in the House of Commons Standing Committee designed to keep the responsibility for the Norwich Navigation in the commissioners' hands. Nor did the commissioners' petition to the Select Committee have any greater success, being held by that committee to be in breach of the principles of the Bill already established by the House of Commons. Various provisions of the Bill, however, gave the commissioners substantial influence over the way in which the Broads Authority would have to discharge its navigation responsibilities.

Having been presented to Parliament on 18th November, 1986, and having had its Second Reading on 1st December of that year, the Bill was taken by the Commons Select Committee in February and March, 1987, and in Standing Committee in July of that year. The General Election then intervened, with the result that the Commons did not give the Bill its Third Reading until November. The Bill then went to the Lords, where it was handled rather more expeditously. It was given a Second Reading on 16th November, was taken in Select Committee on 8th December and was passed on 22nd February, 1988. The Lords' amendments were considered by the Commons on 1st March and Royal Assent was given on the 15th of that month. From beginning to end, therefore, the Bill had taken some sixteen months to become law. It is ironic that after all the pressures applied to prevent amendments being introduced that might have the effect of delaying the Bill, it was now too late to keep to 1st April, 1988, as the operative date for the establishment of the new Authority. The final announcement that the responsible minister made in Parliament was that the operative date would be 1st April, 1989.

★ ★ ★

PART FOUR

THE FUTURE

The Broads   17
Authority: Mark II

The significance of the Broads Authority is that it broke the mould that has confined the system for thirty years to the ten Parks established in the 1950s. By doing so it has opened the door both to the strengthening of the existing National Park authorities, and to the extension of the system to other areas where the county council national park committee is unacceptable or irrelevant.

Ann and Malcolm MacEwen

The passage of the Broads Act and the creation of the new authority gave rise to no little euphoria. The *Eastern Daily Press* hailed the "Dawn of a New Era" and carried a message from Colin Moynihan, then Under-Secretary at the Department of the Environment, stating his belief that "the future of the Broads is, now, at last, secure". No less enthusiastically (allowing for its traditionally sober tone), *The Times* conceded under the caption "The Greening of the Broads" that "everything might be all right here after all". At the official launch of the new authority, its chairman, Jonathan Peel, spoke of a "new and optimistic phase" in the Broads' history and undertook that the restoration programme would be developed as fast as possible. Moira Warland, Director of the NNT was, however, not so confident. She went on record as believing that without conservation being the overriding purpose of the Act, and without conservation groups being represented on the authority, "a lot of its work, if not wasted, will now go into slow motion". That there will continue to be some form of restoration programme seems to be beyond doubt: what is less certain is how fast, how far-reaching and how effective it will be.

On the credit side, the new-style Broads Authority that came into being on 1st April, 1989, is clearly a much stronger body than its predecessor. It is no longer a creature of the local authorities but a statutory body in its own right. It is also a planning authority and has a good deal of planning experience. It has assured access to governmental and local authority finance, it has comprehensive control over navigation and it has a range of powers which correspond to those in force elsewhere by virtue of National Parks and other legislation. It can draw on the accumulation of research and experiment undertaken by its predecessor during the decade of its existence. A particular advantage, given that it is obliged under the legislation to draw up a comprehensive plan within three years of its establishment, is that there is already a Broads Plan compiled and published by the old authority in 1987 on which it will be able to draw.

This Broads Plan set out the agenda which the new authority will presumably follow and develop. It consisted essentially of a survey of the problems and issues facing the authority, grouped under two main headings: wildlife, landscape and history; and tourism and recreation. Within these headings a hundred or so topics were examined and a policy set out for each. A final section, "Implementation", contained passages on finance, consultation, projects and information activities. The whole was well produced and illustrated, and clearly designed to be user-friendly. It was also forthright on a number of issues. The authority undertook to seek to restrict the further growth of motor-boat activities on the Broads, to oppose any drainage schemes or other development that might affect fen and carr of conservation value, and to prohibit the development of boating facilities on the Upper Thurne. On the positive side, it aimed among other things to deal with bank erosion, to encourage proper management of the fens and grazing marshes, to try to reduce river congestion, to conserve appropriate buildings and to ensure sympathetic new development.

Some of the lines along which the new authority is working are already discernible. Bolstered by research that has shown conclusively that even a small reduction in boat speeds results in a significant reduction in wash, it is proposing to reduce maximum speeds on the Broads generally by one mph (although the problem of policing the new limits may not be easy to solve). It is to continue experimentation into forms of bank protection other than piling. It is proposing to continue to spend modest amounts of money on the labour costs of clearing carr woodland and maintaining fen. It is also continuing the programme of mud-pumping silted-up broads, still on an experimental basis. On the other side of the coin— perhaps ominously—it has modified its policy of not permitting the development of permanent moorings for private motor craft to provide for exceptions to the general rule. Another issue which it appears is being tackled is that of landward access to the Broads. There are already a good number of footpaths in Broadland, perhaps some 250 miles in all, and the area is crossed by the long-distance Weavers Way, which runs from Cromer to Yarmouth. But there is danger of erosion through overuse, especially in the peaty soil of the Broadland valleys, while there is a school of thought which maintains that the Broads are essentially for water-based

recreation and that there should be no particular concern for ramblers. Happily, however, it is the policy of the Broads Authority to clear and improve existing footpaths and to establish and maintain a network of circular footpaths in the area. The usual constraints of shortage of funds and uncooperative landowners, however, mean that there is still much to be done.

The outcome of these and other issues will necessarily reflect the priorities which the new authority sets for itself, on which the Broads Act gave no guidance. The extent to which the authority will in practice resolve any particular issue in which the conservation aspect is at odds with recreational, commercial or navigational aspects is still a matter for speculation. The one certain thing is that conflicts are bound to arise, as indeed they did during the life of the old authority even though there was then a clear steer in its terms of reference in favour of conservation; and we have already seen, over the issue of a new bridge at Wroxham, a conflict between conservation and navigation interests, with the Broads Authority itself presenting two incompatible points of view before an inquiry. Much therefore clearly depends on personalities and the balance of membership of the new authority. It is being said of this that although it has a majority of elected local

The Broads Authority's floating mud pump at work on a dyke. The mud is sprayed under high pressure into the adjoining marsh, where the ground is floristically less rich and the mud will do less damage. By the following season, all traces of the pumping will have healed over.
Eastern Daily Press

175

councillors, there is—in the words of Martin Shaw, the Norfolk Chief Planning Officer—"no reason to believe that they will not be extremely sympathetic towards conservation in Broadland". The Chairman of the authority, Jonathan Peel, has also made the entirely valid point that with strong local representation "local people do not feel remote and uncertain". Certainly there is no basis for maintaining that simply because any member represents a special interest or has a particular background he will be biased against competing proposals and policies. Nevertheless an analysis of the membership of the authority is not reassuring. Of its thirty-five members, thirteen are local authority representatives who on the face of it have no particular axe to grind, although the presumption must be that they will mainly have local economic and employment concerns. Another four of the local authority representatives are farmers who, with four of the nine Secretary of State appointees, make a total of eight with farming or landowning interests. There are also nine members with boating or navigational interests of one sort or another. Against this, there is no representative at all of unofficial conservation bodies. It must be said that the Earl of Cranbrook, representing English Nature, and Professor Timothy O'Riordan, representing the Countryside Commission, are both men of considerable eminence who are bound to ensure that a conservation voice is heard, but the general perception is that neither of the bodies they represent is at present disposed to take a strong and positive environmental stance, nor are they working well together.

The composition and influence of the authority's Navigation Committee is also relevant, especially as the boat-hiring associations, which are represented both on it and on the main authority, are on record as arguing for precedence for navigation over conservation on the Broads. The committee is bound to be a powerful influence on the authority for a number of reasons: partly because it is the only specialist committee provided for in the legislation, partly because it has its own source of funds separate from those of the authority as a whole, partly because navigation is bound to be an important if not all-pervasive aspect of the authority's responsibilities, partly because the committee is represented on the full authority by two of its members, and partly because the Act specifies that "the Authority shall have regard to any representations made to it by the Navigation Committee on matters relating to the navigation area". The composition of the committee was carefully laid down in the Act in such a way as to ensure that it would have a majority of members who were not already members of the authority but who in one way or another represented users of the navigation. In fact the composition goes even further than this in that of the total of thirteen members there are no more than four who appear to have no association at all, whether formal or informal, with boating or navigational interests. Given all this, the comments that were expressed during the passage of the Broads Bill through Parliament about the possible bias of the authority in favour of navigational interests are clearly hard to refute. The view is certainly held that the government, when shaping the Act, conceded too much in the face of the prolonged and uncompromising opposition which the Port and Haven Commissioners and others had maintained to the assumption by the authority of navigational powers.

Another area of concern is whether the composition of the authority adequately reflects the national, as opposed to the local, interest. On the one hand, twenty members of the authority are there to represent local organizations of one sort or another, while only four represent bodies—the Countryside Commission, English Nature and the AWA—that have a wider than local concern. Of the remaining twelve members, there are none who need necessarily be local people, although it would be natural to expect that some of them would be, given the requirement that they should represent boating, farming and navigational interests. In practice, the overwhelming majority of the authority appear to be local residents. The normal requirement for a National Park is that it should consist of two-thirds local and one-third national representatives appointed by the Secretary of State. In the case of the Broads, the Secretary of State's list was circumscribed by limitations imposed on him under the Act, which effectively gave him very little room—even if he had been so minded—to include representatives with a national outlook. Given that the Broads are a natural environment that is recognized as nationally, even internationally, important; given that they are a national recreational resource with four hundred thousand people visiting them annually; and given that seventy-five per cent of the authority's main expenditure comes directly from the national exchequer and another twelve per cent or so indirectly from rate support grants, this bias of membership is bound to be seen as questionable. As will have been made evident by the foregoing chapters, a strong thread running through the Broads saga over the past forty years has been the determination of local people and bodies to prevent the Broads coming under the control, or even the undue influence, of outsiders. On this reckoning, local pressures have more than prevailed.

Despite some encouraging signs, therefore, the new authority has yet to show that it is a body that will tackle its problems adequately, even to the limited extent of its resources and powers. As with National Parks generally, resources are still grossly inadequate and there remain areas in which the authority does not even now have the necessary powers, which fall to be exercised, if at all, on a regional, national, or even European level. Nevertheless, the advent of this quasi-National Park after a break of over thirty years has resulted in a degree of optimism on several counts. It is hoped that as well as making more progress locally, it will both provide the impetus for the creation of other National Parks and induce some rethinking of the ways in which Britain currently runs those that already exist. As Ann and Malcolm MacEwen have suggested, the hope is that the existence of the new Broads Authority will be significant not only for the Broads themselves and for their inhabitants, but also in the national context.

There are several questions that are prompted by suggestions of this nature. The first is whether the manner in which the Broads arrangements were brought about may not in fact have inhibited rather than stimulated the creation of others. Certainly the Broads experience to some degree encouraged those who wished to see the extension of National Park designations to areas of Britain which are not at present covered. Marion Shoard, for example, proceeded to call for the creation of further parks in such areas as the New Forest, the South Downs, the Chilterns and parts of Dorset. These are areas of valuable countryside that are not only badly in need of protection, but are also near centres of population and attract large numbers of visitors. As she pointed out, the existing National Parks are for the most part upland moor, whereas it is the lowland countryside, of which the Broads are a prime example, that is mainly under threat. Nevertheless, the problems of designating new parks are all too plain to see. It is true that government policy, as expressed in the 1990 Environment White Paper, is now in favour of the creation of new National Parks. However, after the years of hassle and compromise that the Countryside Commission had to undergo in order to produce even a partial solution for the Broads, it is apparent that they are far from keen to face the entrenched opposition that is to be expected from any further areas that they might wish to designate. The way things are going is clearly shown in *Fit for the Future*, the report prepared by the Countryside Commission's National Parks Review Panel, in which only one new National Park, the New Forest, is proposed. The sad reality is that politically what has happened over the Broads has been profoundly discouraging. It could be argued that the original National Parks initiative had well-nigh petered out before any serious consideration had been given to the Broads and hence that there was some excuse for the long years of inaction, but it could also be maintained that had it not been for the stubborn and prolonged local opposition to the idea of a Broads National Park the whole history of landscape and nature conservation in this country might have been radically different. It cannot now be asserted with any credibility that the Broads experience will provide the impetus for a new round of National Park designations, however desirable these may be.

The extensive controversy over the Broads has also highlighted the inadequacies of the National Parks system as a whole. The National Parks movement was initiated with high ideals—those of protecting tracts of countryside of particular beauty and of making them accessible for public enjoyment and recreation, while preserving the traditional farming and other occupations which existed in them. That, at least, was the theory; the practice has proved very different. The local councils concerned have hung on to their powers and controls, and the parks authorities have never had the strength or independence that they have needed in order to fulfil their intended purposes. They have also been starved of funds: the classic comparison is with the Covent Garden Opera House, the government's grant for which exceeds the total that it spends on the National Parks, even though these are visited by over fifty million people each year. This is not to decry the practice of subsidizing opera but merely to state the case, which ought to be self-evident, for a less élitist order of priorities when it comes to governmental subventions towards leisure activities, particularly when the maintenance of the nation's countryside heritage is at stake. The role of the government has also been highly dubious in other ways. Massive development—quarries, reservoirs, defence installations and training areas, main roads and bypasses, an oil terminal and a nuclear power station—has been allowed to take place in National Parks, to the extent that Lord Strang, a former chairman of the National Parks Commission, was moved to say that "Where a government Department has had plans for erecting large installations of one kind or another in a national park, I can remember no case where it has been diverted from its purpose by anything the Commission might say." Nor is this the end of the story. Agriculture, the intensity of which has developed to a degree that was never imagined by the founders of the National Parks, has been allowed to change their character to an extent that is nothing short of tragic. Small-scale, environmentally sympathetic farming has been permitted to languish, while opportunities for local enterprise and employment have mostly been neglected. On the one hand, the pressure of visitors has been allowed to degrade sensitive areas, while on the other the question of the provision of access and footpaths has never been adequately tackled. Wholly inappropriate development proposals have been approved while traditional settlements and buildings have been left unprotected.

For the most part, the question whether the Broads have broken this mould has to be answered mainly in the negative. As we have seen, throughout the preparation and passage of the Broads

Act the government, with the support of the local councils and various lobbies, insisted on conformity with existing National Parks provisions, even where there was some doubt about their continuing validity. In no instance was there an attempt at improvement, let alone innovation. The Broads are, therefore, largely subject to the legal, structural and financial limitations that affect the National Parks as a whole. Worse than this, the effects of such changes as were dictated by the particular circumstances of the Broads have involved a dilution of the National Parks model. Conservation is not an overriding concern, the national interest is worse represented and a weight is accorded to navigational interests that unbalances the representation on the authority as a whole. Altogether, therefore, the Broads cannot be regarded as an example of the way in which any existing or future National Park should be developed, but should be seen rather as a pointer to the reforms that are still needed if the National Parks system is to serve the national interest adequately. Sadly, *Fit for the Future* fails also to address these reforms, which must above all involve some resolution of the competing requirements of conservation on the one hand and recreation and other uses on the other.

What can be said, however, is that there were significant advances in the early years of the old Broads Authority, with the launching of an unprecedented programme of research and experiment into the crucial problem of water quality, and with the culmination of the Halvergate controversy in the Broads Grazing Marshes Conservation Scheme and its transition to the concept of ESAs. Imperfect and incomplete as these developments were, they were steps in the right direction. Their importance should not be underestimated in a country that is currently grappling with two major problems: water supply and drainage, and land use management in the countryside. It is to these two key questions, as well as to the locally even more critical one of preventing a new marine inundation of Broadland, that the final chapter turns.

★　★　★

Dawn of a New Era?   18

The measures necessary for protecting the national parks are but one part of a national system for the conservation and enjoyment of the countryside. It is not too much to say that, in the long run, unless the entire countryside is managed in the spirit of conserving its living and non-living resources, the specially protected "sensitive areas" will be unlikely to survive. The idea that islands of nature and of scenic beauty can prosper in a sea of destructive practices and a climate of ignorance, greed and philistinism is fatally flawed.

Ann and Malcolm MacEwen

The first of the major problems that the new authority has to address is the absolutely crucial one of water quality. As we have seen, the problems have been researched and are now mostly understood, and tentative steps have been taken towards solving them. Clearly it would be unrealistic to suppose that it will be possible for the foreseeable future to restore the broads to their wholly unpolluted, Phase I condition. One reason is that the leaching of nitrates off farmland is a slow process and one which would be likely to continue for many decades, even if the use of fertilizers throughout the Broads catchment area were to cease tomorrow. One estimate is that not much more than about one tenth of the nitrogen that is added to crops actually ends up in foodstuffs, much of the remainder eventually finding its way into groundwater. On this reckoning, there is an inordinate amount of nitrate still to percolate from East Anglian farmland into the broads and it is being added to all the time. Realistically, the best that can be expected is a halt to the outflow of phosphates from the relevant sewage works and hence, we may hope, a reversion to something like the Phase II, partly eutrophicated conditions that existed at the end of the Second World War.

During the nineteen-eighties, at the instigation of the Broads Authority, the AWA made a start by installing phosphate-stripping equipment at several of their sewage works on the Ant and the Bure. Now that the water industry has been privatized, their willingness to continue the programme—given the pressures for profits and the competing demands for capital investment that they face, not least in removing nitrates from drinking water— is clearly in doubt. In the short term, the situation might even have deteriorated in the light of the temporary relaxations in water quality standards that the AWA, among others, were granted at the outset of privatisation, to enable them to undertake the much needed capital investment in water supply. Fortunately, it does not seem that any relaxations were needed on the Broads. Nevertheless, the programme of phosphate stripping on the northern rivers, which it was hoped would be substantially complete within a few years, has now ground to a halt, and there appears to be little prospect of any early start with a similar programme on the Yare. A report submitted by the Broads Authority to the Royal Commission on Environmental Pollution in the spring of 1990 suggests that phosphorus levels are again increasing and that the broads are filling with sediment at the rate of about two centimetres a year, which would mean that they would cease to exist in about fifty years' time. Suction dredging of phosphate-enriched sediments will be a necessary part of any restoration process—in Barton and Hickling Broads, for example, the build-up of sediment is already creating problems for navigation—but will be a waste of resources if the cleansing of inflows is not also undertaken. The failure to press ahead with the phosphate stripping pro-

Towards a solution to the problem of water quality. Transfer of ferric sulphate for phosphate stripping at Stalham sewage works.
Norfolk Naturalists' Trust

gramme is now a cause for considerable concern, from the navigational as well as from the environmental point of view, and poses the question whether there is in fact any longer a serious intention to improve water quality in the Broads.

Throughout this book, the problems of trying to preserve areas of particular landscape and wildlife interest in a generally polluted Broads environment have been described. In a somewhat wider context, the current doctrine seems to be that attempts to conserve nature and landscape in the Broads as a whole must be confined to the executive area of the authority, to the exclusion of any substantive interest in the countryside around. Moreover, as we have seen, as a result of pressures by local authorities and the farming community, the government conceded that the authority's remit should cover just about the smallest conceivable area, despite the fact that previous reviewers, in particular Hobhouse and the Broads Consortium Committee, had envisaged the inclusion of a fair amount of surrounding countryside. Put crudely, the view that prevailed was that the land was for farming, and that tourists, car-parks and the rest should be kept as far away as possible. The result has been that for the most part the boundary has been drawn along the edge of the flood plain, while the fields and woods on the slopes that form the backdrop to the Broads landscape have been rigorously excluded. There are, nevertheless, a number of cogent reasons, both local and national, why a new look needs to be taken at the related issues of the limits of the Broads Authority's executive area and the farming regime within the region. The Prince of Wales made a key point about the future of the Broads when, after a visit in April, 1989, he said in a message to the Broads Authority, "I very much hope that before long it will be possible to include a somewhat wider area in the National Park so that the unique nature of the Broads can be properly maintained and restored."

The Broads Authority has already achieved a good deal in preventing the further degradation of the Broads landscape and natural environment. Since the adoption of the Broads Grazing Marshes Conservation Scheme and, subsequently, the ESA arrangements, a substantial take-up of compensation has been recorded, to the extent of some eighty-three per cent of the eligible area by 1988, even if there has not so far been any significant recovery from arable of those areas lost to grazing land before the arrangements were on offer. There are also now some further grounds for optimism. A "third tier" ESA has been introduced which would allow for increased payments in return for the maintenance of higher water levels on grazing marsh over the winter and spring. The European Community also appears to be willing to fund environmental improvements in Special Protection

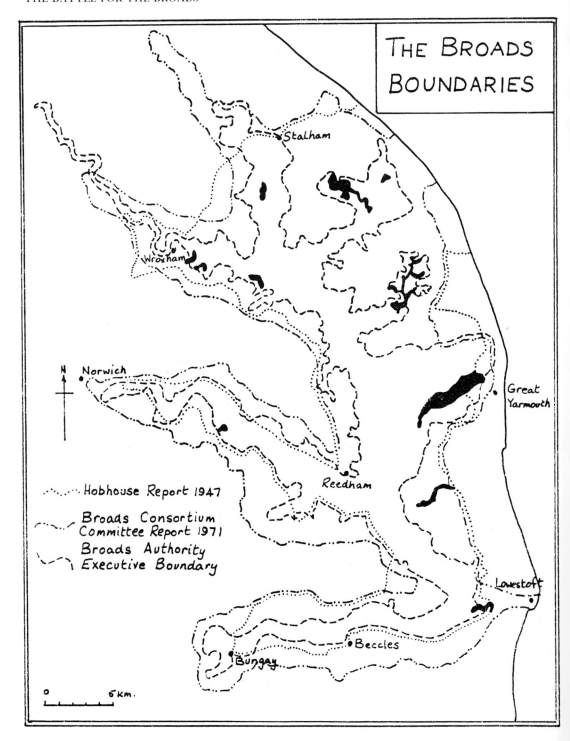

THE BROADS
BOUNDARIES

Stalham

Wroxham

N

Norwich

Great
Yarmouth

Reedham

.... Hobhouse Report 1947

Broads Consortium
Committee Report 1971
Broads Authority
Executive Boundary

Lowestoft

Beccles

Bungay

0   5 km.

Areas (which could include SSSIs and possibly other areas in the Broads) created under the terms of the Bern Convention on the Conservation of European Wildlife and Natural Habitats, which the UK ratified in 1983. On the other hand, there has been no attempt to remedy the degradation that has been caused by intensive farming on the slopes and uplands surrounding the flood plains of Broadland proper. The catchment area of the Broads rivers is so large that it would be unrealistic to expect that it should all be counted in, even if there now seems to be some prospect that the ESA may be extended further up the river valleys. But if Broadland is really to be restored to a semblance of its former self, the attempt must be made to rescue more of its visually and environmentally degraded farmland, on its periphery as well as within it. The prospect of sensitive and ecologically sound management of a Broadland which includes the farms, smallholdings, and woodlands on the surrounding uplands is not one that should be lightly dismissed. An important aspect is that if the land leading up to the immediate watersheds of the Broads were to cease to be intensively farmed, the further percolation of fertilizers and herbicides through their side streams would cease. The abstraction of water for agricultural irrigation and other purposes, with the accompanying lowering of the water table in the underlying chalk, is also a matter for concern and is unlikely to be without its consequences for the Broads. The nub of the case is set out in the quotation at the head of this chapter. In the last resort, it will not be possible to maintain an environmentally inviolate Broadland in degraded surroundings. The tragedy is that it is patently too late to do anything about the Broadland villages, which should have been designated as conservation areas years ago. Our descendants will wonder why—when Norfolk brick, reed and pantiles can combine into an exceptionally pleasing style of architecture that would allow sympathetic modern adaptations— we have allowed the Broads villages to degenerate into a mess of shoddy bungalosis and pretentious "executive" housing, as well as an uncontrolled rash of unsightly farming and other structures.

There are also compulsions of national scope that affect the situation and that should provide an opportunity to rescue more of Broadland and its surroundings, if anyone is sufficiently imaginative to work out some suitable arrangements. In the country at large, a fundamental change of outlook is currently taking place over the whole complex of agricultural and environmental issues. Restrictions are being set, and will progressively spread and intensify, on the use of artificial fertilizers, herbicides and pesticides. Grants for capital "improvements", the effects of which have been environmentally damaging, have lapsed. The prospect of the continuing overproduction of foodstuffs to an extent that is becoming both financially and morally insupportable has resulted in the introduction first of "set-aside" and then of levels of compensation for varying types of "environmentally sensitive" land management. All the signs are that the limits to overproduction are going to be progressively tighter and that the amount of land applied to farming is going to have to be very considerably reduced over the coming years. One estimate is that something of the order of three to four million hectares of land will be surplus by the end of the century. There is therefore a developing realization, not least in the farming community, that some form of financial support other than subsidies on unwanted crops is going to be increasingly required nationwide.

The question that has now to be addressed is how this surplus is to be managed without the dereliction of vast areas of the countryside and ruinous financial pressures on the farming community. On this, a fascinating policy statement was issued in 1988 by the Royal Society for Nature Conservation. It made a powerful case for the development of nature conservation as an alternative land use, which it urges should become an "acceptable way of earning a living in the countryside of the future". This approach has since been endorsed by the CPRE, who have proposed the replacement of European production-linked subsidies by environmental management payments. In the Royal Society for Nature Conservation's paper, the case is made for the establishment in the first instance of this type of farming (which it calls "heritage farming") by "environmentally strategic" farmers, that is those farming on land with "special conservation potential". Important criteria would be the proximity of these farms to nature reserves or areas of semi-natural habitats, or their existence in areas of basic resource constraints or hazards (such as liability to flooding). In the summer of 1991, the Government announced a "Countryside Stewardship Scheme", entailing the expenditure of £13 million over three years on grants to farmers designed to preserve and restore "especially valuable landscapes" across the country, ranging from moorland to grazing marshes, reedbeds and coastal vegetation. As a response to the case made by the RSNC and CPRE, this can only be described as a marginal initiative, tightly encased in a Treasury straitjacket. But at least it is a beginning; and there is no doubt that the Broads and their periphery would, with a little imagination and application, be eminently suited to the introduction of adaptations of this nature.

As for the adoption of any wider definition of the Broads area, there are several obvious problems, particularly so soon after the passage of the Broads Act. One is that of the biological restoration of the areas that need to be reclaimed from intensive use. This problem is well understood in the United States and solutions have been applied there to wetlands as well as to prairie. Given the necessary research and experiment, there is no reason why the concept should not also be applied in this country, recreating such areas as the lost Broads grazing marshes or even some of the original undrained fen, as well as areas presently being intensively farmed. The Broads Authority is already in the business of shipping reedfen to Cleveland, both to establish beds there and to clear its own beds for renewal. There seems no reason why the process could not also be applied within Broadland itself.

Another problem may be that of the political mechanics. The Countryside Stewardship Scheme might provide the right model, but it might be preferable formally to extend the area controlled by the Broads Authority, so that the whole range of safeguards and benefits could come into play. If so, it should not be beyond the bounds of possibility to revive, in a suitably adapted form, the arrangement under which the local authorities ceded to the former Broads Authority the necessary powers over a defined area of countryside. By such a means, extra areas of land could, at least in theory, fairly readily be added to those already controlled by the authority under the provisions of the legislation. Alternatively, some more informal arrangements could perhaps be agreed between the authority and some if not all of the district councils, without necessarily involving any formal transfer of powers. If a way is to be found of somehow extending the effective Broads area, the main problem would clearly be that of motivation, since there is no doubt that the idea will attract very stiff opposition. The only hope is that the farming community in and around the Broads should be persuaded by a combination of effective inducements and a perception of deteriorating prospects facing them that the undertaking of environmentally sound management is the most attractive option available.

Meanwhile, an urgent, if localized, challenge is that of the Hickling/Horsey/Martham Ramsar Site. The complex of problems affecting this site has been described earlier. At the moment a number of initiatives are in train. One is the removal of drainage board dykes from within the Hickling reserve to its periphery, so that the water levels can be raised. This appears to be dependent on funding by English Nature. The NNT have also been purchasing further land adjoining their existing holdings, so that they have more control over the drainage regime. There is also the prospect that the "third tier" ESA arrangements may be targeted on the Upper Thurne catchment area. The Broads Authority has been trying to create "no go" zones for boats, part permanent and part seasonal, so as to reduce the disturbance to wildfowl. However, opposition from boating interests has caused the proposal to be modified, so that it is now only a three-year experimental scheme, extending over an area no greater than that previously covered by voluntary arrangements initiated by the NNT. Looking at the whole picture, there is now some prospect of progress being made, albeit without the overall determination which is needed to recreate a real "wetland wilderness".

The final problem concerns sea defences and the dangers of flooding. Broadland has had a long history of flooding and underwent a very nasty experience in 1953, when wide areas were inundated. There is continuing danger of another surge in the North Sea, traditionally caused by a low pressure area passing north of Scotland across to Scandinavia with accompanying northerly winds funnelling water into the shallow seas lying between East Anglia and the Continent. Ever since 1953 there has been a realization both that there is a danger of recurrence and that Broadland's network of sea walls and embankments is deteriorating and becoming increasingly unreliable as a line of defence. In 1976, therefore, the AWA commissioned a feasibility study by Rendel Palmer and Tritton to assess how best to reduce the effects of surge tides in the Broads rivers system. The study considered three main solutions: protection by flood embankments with additional tidal washlands, a tidal barrier at Yarmouth complete with sluices and a lock, and a surge-excluding barrier, the latter on the grounds that it would entail the least capital cost and would be the most economic solution when costs and benefits were taken together. To do them justice, the consultants rejected the tidal barrier partly on the grounds that the conversion of the Broads to a non-tidal, freshwater system would have far-reaching ecological effects, while the surge barrier would be environmentally beneficial in that it would prevent exceptional incursions of salt water into the system. Nevertheless the study was heavily criticized for not sufficiently considering the environmental issues involved, the main contention being that the scheme would give enough security to farmers in the low-lying areas to encourage them to convert grazing marsh to arable. It was in fact estimated that a surge barrier would have enabled some 45,000 hectares to be converted to arable, assisted by an eighty-five per cent grant from the Ministry of Agriculture. In a sense, therefore, the idea for the scheme foreshadowed the Halvergate controversy. Partly for environmental reasons, but partly also on account of opposition from Yarmouth and from the Port and Haven Commissioners, it came to nothing at that time.

More than a decade later, however, the problem has not gone away. In 1987 the AWA reckoned that after years of neglect something between £20 million and £50 million was needed for embankment repairs. In 1989 the National Rivers Authority revived the idea of a barrier and estimated at the same time that

some £12 million was needed to protect the Broads coastline between Happisburgh and Winterton. This was irrespective of what might or might not happen to sea levels as a result of the "greenhouse effect". The slide rules and computers have therefore once again been in use, and consultants have been reviewing a number of possible options, including: (a) a surge-excluding barrier at Yarmouth, (b) a barrier on the Bure with a flood reservoir at Haddiscoe Island, (c) heightened and improved embankments generally and (d) the use of washlands to draw off surplus water. It would be no exaggeration to say that the whole future of the Broads is dependent on a solution, possibly one consisting of a combination of these options, being found. Several problems, however, remain. One is that the most profitable option, if one calculates on a standard cost/benefit basis and ignores the long term environmental effects, seems to be simply to leave the Broads to their fate. Another is the cost of any alternative solution. The latest estimate by the NRA appears to be that some £13 million a year may be required over a ten year period, 35 per cent of which would under present arrangements fall to be paid by the local authorities. This is clearly an impossible task and increased

Horsey Dunes. These low marram dunes are all that protects the Thurne broads from the North Sea. It was at this point, where the old Hundred Stream used to flow into the sea, that the dunes were breached in 1939, with disastrous results.
M. K. Ewans

189

Opposite: *Horsey Mill.*
J. J. Buxton

government funding is going to be needed. Altogether, there is clearly still a long way to go before the Broads are secure.

The main points of the agenda for the Broads are thus clear, even if the existence of the will and the resources are less so. The Broads must be preserved as a place for waterborne and land-based recreation, with the employment which depends on it, but with an eye for recreation not being permitted to damage the fragile environment on which everything ultimately depends—and here some form of differential environmental tax on boats, as is practised in Canada and elsewhere, needs to be seriously considered. The fens and their waterways need a greater degree of management to re-create further the conditions in which they provided a rich and diverse habitat for many species of flora and fauna. The water quality needs to be restored, at least to the standards of fifty years ago. Steps need to be taken to put an end to the deep draining of land in and around the immediate catchment areas of the Broads complex. The question of the Broads boundary and the nature of farming along the surrounding slopes needs to be addressed. Incentives for the restoration of grazing marsh and of an environmentally sympathetic farming regime in and around the Broads need to be implemented. The problem of the deterioration of the sea and river defences is becoming urgent.

The pictorial and literary accounts that have come down to us show that a century ago the Broads were a unique and beautiful place. The damage and degradation that they have suffered at our hands have been extreme, no less than the complacent and self-serving attitudes that have for so long prevented anything positive being done. There could, however, now be an opportunity to restore them to something of their former glory.

★ ★ ★

Further Reading

Many of the books that have been written about the Broads have been mentioned in the text. Of the general works, undoubtedly the most attractive is W. A. Dutt's *The Norfolk Broads* (Methuen, 1903), while the most authoritative (although now a little dated), is Ted Ellis's *The Broads* (Collins, 1965). Other "portraits" of the Broads that have been published over the years include:

Davies, G. C. *Norfolk Broads and Rivers*. Blackwood, 1883.
Manning, S. A. *Portrait of Broadland*. Hale, 1980.
Mottram, R. H. *The Broads*. Hale, 1952.
Suffling, E. R. *The Land of the Broads*. Perry, 1885.
Wentworth Day, J. *Marshland Adventure*. Harrap, 1950.
Wentworth Day, J. *Portrait of the Broads*. Hale, 1967.

As indicated in the text, two of the most rewarding books about the former way of life and activities on the Broads are Oliver Ready's *Life and Sport on the Norfolk Broads in the Golden Days* (Laurie, 1910) and Nicholas Everitt's *Broadland Sport* (Everitt, 1900).

Books about Norfolk wherries include not only Frank Carr's *Sailing Barges* (Terence Dalton, 1989) but also Roy Clark's *Black-Sailed Traders* (Putnam, 1961) and Robert Malster's *Wherries and Waterways* (Terence Dalton, 1986). The latter also describes the history of the various East Anglian "navigations", as does *The Canals of Eastern England*, by John Boyes and Ronald Russell (David & Charles, 1977).

Books about the wildlife of East Anglia and the Broads are legion, many of the most fascinating being mentioned in the text. As may be evident, my own favourites are Emma Turner's *Broadlands Birds* (Country Life, 1924) and Jim Vincent's *A Season of Birds* (Weidenfeld & Nicholson, 1980), while S. A. Manning's *Nature in East Anglia* (World's Work, 1976) provides a useful overview and suggests further sources.

Biographies of Sir Thomas Browne and the Reverend Richard Lubbock are contained in Thomas Southwell's editions of their works: *Browne, Sir Thomas. Notes and Letters on the Natural History of Norfolk, with Notes by Thomas Southwell FZS* (Jarrold and Sons, 1902) and *Lubbock, R. Observations on the Fauna of Norfolk, and more particularly on the District of the Broads, with Notes by Thomas Southwell FZS* (Stacy, 1879). There are two biographies of Arthur Patterson, S. A. Manning's *Broadland Naturalist* (Soman-Wherry, 1948) and Beryl Tooley's *John Knowlittle. The Life of the Yarmouth Naturalist Arthur Henry Patterson ALS* (Wilson-Poole, 1985). Ted Ellis is featured in Eugene Stone's *Ted Ellis. The People's Naturalist* (Jarrold Colour Publications, 1988).

Books about Broads photographers include *Life and Landscape: P. H. Emerson* by N. McWilliam and V. Sekules (Sainsbury Centre for Visual Arts, 1986), *The Broadland Photographers* by C. S. Middleton (Wensum,

1978) and *P. H. Emerson, Photographer of Norfolk* by Peter Turner and Richard Wood. Of Emerson's own works, those which feature Broadland are *Life and Landscape on the Norfolk Broads* (with T. F. Goodall) (Sampson Lowe, 1986); *Idyls of the Norfolk Broads* (Autotype Company, 1888); *On English Lagoons* (Nutt, 1893); and *Marsh Leaves* (Nutt, 1895).

Arthur Ransome's two Broadland classics are *Coot Club* (Cape, 1936) and *The Big Six* (Cape, 1940). An attractive account of Ransome and his books is contained in Christina Hardyment's *Arthur Ransome and Captain Flint's Trunk* (Cape, 1984).

The early history of the conservation movement in Britain is well covered in Sir Dudley Stamp's *Nature Conservation in Britain* (Collins, 1969) and John Sheail's *Nature in Trust. The History of Nature Conservation in Britain* (Blackie, 1976). The two authoritative books about the National Parks are Ann and Malcolm MacEwen's *National Parks: Conservation or Cosmetics?* (Allen & Unwin, 1982) and their later book *Greenprints for the Countryside* (Allen & Unwin, 1987). A shorter, illustrated discussion of the National Parks is contained in Brian Redhead's *The National Parks of England and Wales* (Oxford Illustrated Press, 1988).

The Halvergate saga is partially covered in *Countryside Conflicts* by Philip Lowe and others (Gower, 1986) and in *Taming the Flood* by Jeremy Purseglove (Oxford University Press, 1989).

Books on countryside and conservation issues have proliferated during the past decade. Some of the more recent include:

Adams, W. M. *Nature's Place*. Allen & Unwin, 1986.

Blunden, J., and Curry, N. *A Future for our Countryside*. Blackwell, 1988.

Countryside Commission. *New Opportunities for the Countryside*. CCP 224, 1987.

Countryside Commission. *Fit for the Future*. Report of the National Parks Review Panel. CCP 334, 1991.

Moore, N. W. *The Bird of Time, the Science and Politics of Nature Conservation*. Cambridge, 1987.

Pye-Smith, C., and Hall, C. *The Countryside We Want*. Green Books, 1987.

Shoard, M. *This Land is Our Land: the Struggle for Britain's Countryside*. Palladin, 1987.

Index

Illustrations in **bold type**